BUILDING CONSTRUCTION

BUILDING CONSTRUCTION
FOR NATIONAL CERTIFICATE

by
E. G. WARLAND,
M.I.Struct.E.

Volume I
(First Year Course)   6/6 net

' The principle of illustrating the various details of construction in isometric projection is a good one and should be of great help to both student and teacher. . . . All the details are well described.

' The arrangement of the text as an abbreviated form of notes is a welcome departure from the usual practice in books on building construction of allowing the written to exceed the illustrative matter.

' A book that can be recommended with confidence.'

The Technical Journal.

Volume II
(Second Year Course)   6/6 net

' As efficient, as lucid and as helpful as the first volume. All the author's knowledge of the needs of students—the result of practical experience in teaching—has been embodied in this series which can be confidently recommended.'

The Parthenon.

Volume III
(Third Year Course)   6/6 net

' The book . . . gives in very clear detail, both by drawing and written word, concise information on building procedure. The splendid sketches . . . give special weight to the work of the author. We hope the possessors of Volumes 1 and 2 will purchase No. 3. The volumes are the embodiment of sound teaching and can be recommended with emphasis.'

Journal of the Incorporated
Clerks of Works Association.

BUILDING CONSTRUCTION

FOR NATIONAL CERTIFICATE

VOLUME I
(First Year Course)

By

E. G. WARLAND
M.I.Struct.E.
Head of the Department of Building and Architecture,
City Technical College, Liverpool
Author of ' Modern Practical Masonry,' and
' The Fabric of Modern Buildings '
Examiner in Building Construction
Union of Lancashire and Cheshire Institutes

Published by
HODDER AND STOUGHTON LIMITED
for THE ENGLISH UNIVERSITIES PRESS LTD.
LONDON

The paper and binding
of this book conform to the
authorized economy standard

Made and Printed in Great Britain for the English Universities Press, Ltd.,
by Butler & Tanner Ltd., Frome and London

PREFACE

THIS book is the first of a series of three which are intended to cover the first three years' syllabus of a National Certificate Course.

The object of this book is to encourage the study of building construction and to place in the hands of teachers and students a book which can be used as a class-book.

Also, it has been compiled to meet the requirements of students who are preparing for the various professional examinations in which the study of building construction forms part of the syllabus.

No attempt has been made to deal with any of the phases of modern construction, because it is important that a student who is commencing the study of building construction should become acquainted with the fundamental principles of construction and traditional methods of building.

The author has endeavoured to assist the student to visualise the combination of constructional units by arranging the illustrations in the form of isometric sketches and with particular reference to a complete building.

The text is arranged in an abbreviated form of notes and includes a brief outline of the manufacture and uses of the various building materials illustrated throughout this volume.

The author wishes to express his thanks to the architects Messrs. Medcalf & Medcalf, FF.R.I.B.A., for the use of the scale drawings of the proposed Hall, and to his son Douglas for his assistance in the preparation of the drawings.

E. G. W.

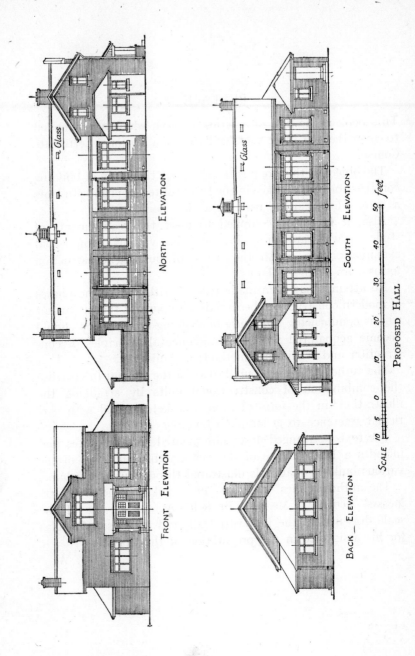

NORTH ELEVATION

Glass

FRONT ELEVATION

SOUTH ELEVATION

Glass

BACK ELEVATION

SCALE 10 5 0 10 20 30 40 50 feet

PROPOSED HALL

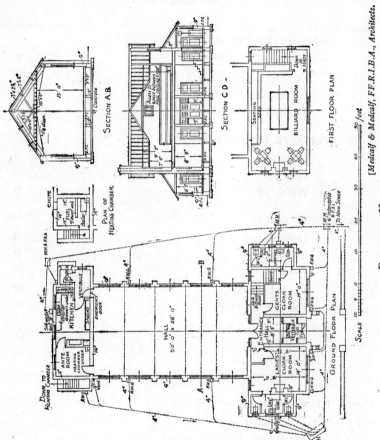

SECTION A.B.

SECTION C.D.

PLAN OF HEATING CHAMBER

FIRST FLOOR PLAN

Space between roof and ceiling flat.

BILLIARD ROOM

SEATING AREA

CHUTE

FUEL

Boiler

DOWN TO HEATING CHAMBER

MH & FAA

KITCHEN

VESTIBULE

EMERGENCY DOOR

ANTE ROOM

HEATING CHAMBER UNDER

HALL
50' 0" x 28' 0"

B

A

ENTRANCE HALL

GENTS CLOAK ROOM

LADIES

CLOAK ROOM

GROUND FLOOR PLAN

TO MAIN SEWER

SCALE   10   5   0   10   20   30   40   50 feet

PROPOSED HALL

[Medcalf & Medcalf, FF.R.I.B.A., Architects.

CONTENTS

LIST OF ILLUSTRATIONS

xiii

CHAPTER I

PRELIMINARY OPERATIONS

THE preliminary steps in building construction are :
[1] The selection of a site.
[2] Testing to ascertain the nature and bearing-capacity of
the ground upon which the foundations are to be imposed.
The cost of a building will be influenced by the type of foundation necessary.

A general examination of the site, including its contours,
should be made, and the roads, railways and drainage indicated
on a plan layout.

Trial pits should be dug at a number of points on the site
and notes made of the nature, levels, thicknesses and inclination of the strata.

Information should be obtained of any made-up ground and
its depth, together with the nature of the soil underlying it,
and the presence of hidden water, if any, and its level should
be noted.

Natural foundation beds should be incompressible or equally
yielding over the whole area and not subjected to atmospheric
or other influences which may alter its nature or powers to
resist the loads to be placed upon them.

The strata, except where piles are used, should be at right
angles to the pressure which is to be placed upon them.

Levelling

Preliminary to constructing concrete foundations, the site
may be required to be levelled and quantities of loose earth
removed to other positions on the site.

A complete survey will indicate the direction and means
of access and position of roads which may govern the position
of floor levels and indicate the amount of excavation necessary.

Subsoils

Rock.—When rock forms the foundation bed it is usually sufficient to cut the rock to form a level bed and fill in all cavities and fissures with concrete.

Solid and ordinary clays make a good foundation bed and will carry heavy loads, but they must be kept fairly dry and protected from atmospheric influences.

Sand will make a good foundation bed if it is confined and kept free from water scouring.

Gravel has high compressive resisting qualities and is not affected by atmospheric influences.

Setting Out Trenches

This is done by pegging out their position on the ground, making sure that offsets are measured from axial lines and that frontage lines are placed in their correct position relative to local requirements. The position of cross walls should be

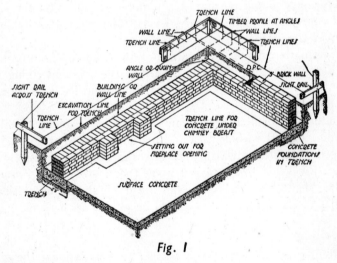

Fig. 1

measured along the main walls and squared from these walls if desired, the total width of trenches being carefully outlined.

Sighting rails may be erected at the corners of a building to determine the correct position for the trenches, as shown in Fig. 1.

The excavation of trenches for the concrete foundations of walls is a necessary preliminary operation to the construction of walls.

Levels should be obtained from a fixed datum point previously determined by the Surveyor and the depth of the trenches being regulated by measurements taken from this datum point.

The bottom of all trenches should be well rammed before the concrete is placed in position.

Timbering Trenches

The soil at the sides of trenches is often required to be supported by a system of timbering.

The system to be adopted will vary according to the depth

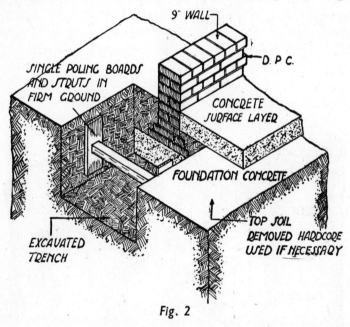

Fig. 2

of the trench and the material which has to be supported. For ordinary trenches, in moderately firm soil a system of poling boards, placed vertically against the sides of the trench, and at intervals of about 6′ centres, is usually sufficient.

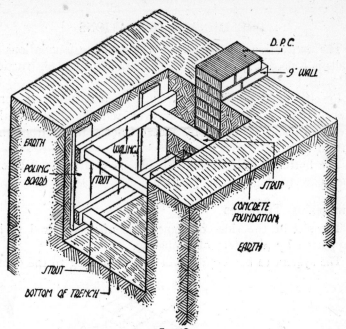

Fig. 3

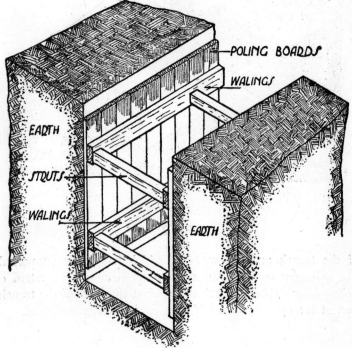

Fig. 4

The poling boards are wedged against the sides of the trench by timber struts, as shown in Fig. 2.

The distance between the poling boards is determined by the conditions prevailing and the nature of the soil. In loose soil a third system of timbering, known as walings, are placed against the poling boards in a horizontal position and strutted as shown in Fig. 3. The use of walings will tend to reduce the number of struts.

In very loose soils and running sands, etc., close boarding or sheeting is used in addition to walings and struts, as shown in Fig. 4.

CHAPTER II

CONCRETE FOUNDATIONS

THE term foundation usually applies to that part of a structure which is below the base of walls, piers, etc., and includes the ground upon which the base of the structure stands.

The latter should be referred to as the foundation bed, and the former as the concrete foundation.

Before proceeding with the construction of foundations, reference should be made to the local building by-laws.

Students should obtain a copy of these by-laws and carefully peruse the sections concerned.

Depth for Concrete Foundations

Where special circumstances or requirements do not exist, the following may be taken as a guide.

In ordinary soils 3'.
In clay soils 4'.
In gravel soils 2'.

Unless the foundation bed is composed of rock, it is necessary to place a bed of concrete immediately beneath the base of walls, piers, etc.

The width of concrete foundations should be such that the loads will be equally distributed over an area of ground which will safely support them.

Thickness of Concrete Foundations

The concrete foundations of walls should not be less than 9" thick and project at least 4" on either side of the lowest course of footings.

For walls comprising two-storey houses or similar buildings, this rule usually provides a base of ample size, but it does not make provision for the width in relation to the bearing value of the foundation bed, or for the thickness of the concrete to resist fracture. In exceptional cases the thickness of the concrete should be obtained by calculation, but in practice

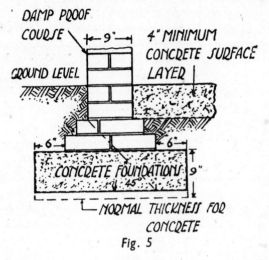

Fig. 5

for ordinary purposes, the thickness of the concrete may be obtained by one of the graphical methods. It has been ascertained that fractures in concrete foundations usually

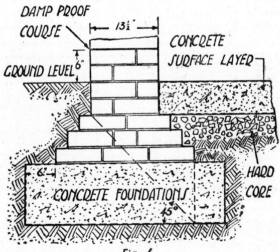

Fig. 6

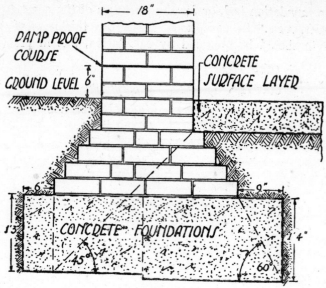

Fig. 7

occur in a direction corresponding to an angle of 45° from the face of the wall. For determining the thickness of concrete foundations under brick walls by graphical methods reference should be made to Figs. 5, 6 and 7.

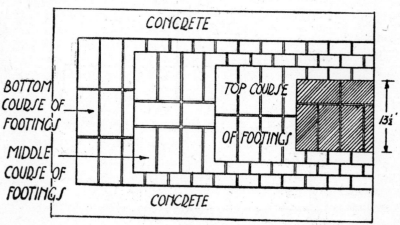

Fig. 8

CHAPTER III

BRICKWORK

BRICKWORK may be described as the grouping of bricks to form a homogeneous mass by the aid of mortar and the general arrangement of the units.

Definitions

The following terms and definitions should be understood before attempting to learn the various methods of bonding in brickwork.

In general, a brick may be assumed to measure $9'' \times 4\frac{1}{2}'' \times 3''$, but these sizes vary and allowance has to be made for the width of the mortar joints.

In the south of England and the Midlands, brickwork rises four courses to the foot, but in some of the Northern Counties brick sizes ensuring a rise of four courses to $13''$ including mortar joints is preferred.

Terms

Stretcher.—The longest face of a brick.

Header.—The end or short face of a brick, approximately half the length of a stretcher.

Half Bat.—Half of a stretcher brick.

Three-quarter Bat.—Three-quarters of a stretcher brick.

Queen Closer.—A brick cut to show $2\frac{1}{4}'' \times 3''$ at each end.

King Closer.—A brick cut to show a header at one end and $2\frac{1}{4}''$ face at the other end.

Quoin.—Is the external angle of a wall.

Course.—Includes all bricks between two consecutive horizontal mortar joints.

Bed Joint.—The mortar joint between two courses.

Cross Joint or Perpends.—The short vertical joints at right-angles to and connecting the bed joints.

Bond is the arrangement of bricks which has for its object the strength of the work as a whole.

English and Flemish bonds are the arrangements most commonly used.

English bond may be considered superior to **Flemish bond** for strength, but the latter produces a better appearance in the finished face-work.

English Bond.—The bricks are arranged in alternate courses of headers and stretchers, as in Figs. 9, 10 and 11.

The centre of a header in one course should fall in the centre of a stretcher in the course above and below it. A $2\frac{1}{4}''$ closer

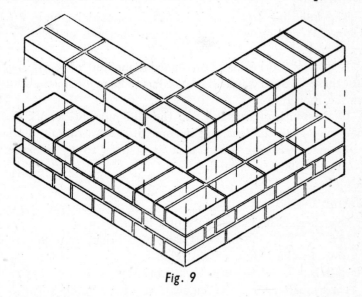

Fig. 9

should be placed next to the quoin header thus displacing the bricks $2\frac{1}{4}''$ to form the face bonding.

Sometimes it is advisable to use a three-quarter bat as the quoin brick in each course instead of a full brick and a closer, as shown in Fig. 18.

In English bond, the rule governing the relation between the face-work and the backing is as follows:

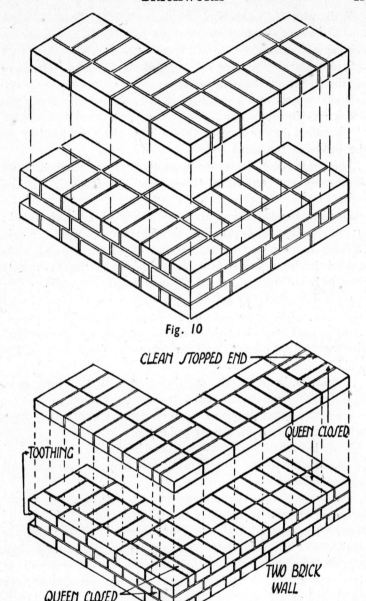

Fig. 10

Fig. 11

Walls which are a multiple whole brick in thickness, headers on the face of the wall should have headers on the inside in the same course.

Stretchers on the face of the wall should have stretchers on the inside in the same course.

Walls which are a multiple half-brick in thickness, the following rule applies :

Stretchers on the face of the wall should have headers on the inside in the same course and vice-versa.

The transverse joints in a wall built in English bond should continue unbroken throughout the thickness of the wall.

Flemish Bond.—There are two kinds of Flemish bond : (1) Single Flemish bond ; (2) Double Flemish bond. Single Flemish bond is a composite bond of Flemish facing with English backing, and consists in arranging the bricks so that they have an appearance of Flemish bond externally. This type of bonding may be adopted for economic reasons and especially where expensive facing bricks are specified.

In double Flemish bond the bricks in each course are arranged alternatively as headers and stretchers on both sides of the wall.

A quarter bond is obtained by placing a $2\frac{1}{4}''$ closer next to the quoin headers, as shown in Figs. 12, 13 and 14.

There are other types of bonding for brickwork but these will be dealt with in a later volume.

Many local building by-laws require that brick footings shall be constructed at the base of walls and that the footings shall rest on concrete.

The projection of the footings on each side of a wall should be at least equal to one-half the thickness of the wall at its base so that the bottom course of footings shall be twice the thickness of the wall above, and each successive course shall increase in regular offsets of $2\frac{1}{4}''$ on each side of the wall, as shown in Figs. 5, 6 and 7. Brick footings provide greater stability against over-turning and they tend to secure a minimum and more uniform settlement of walls.

The height from the bottom course of footings to the base

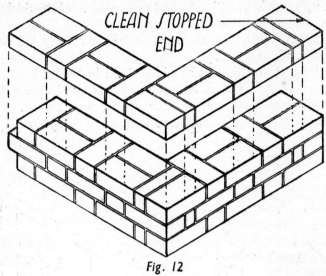

Fig. 12

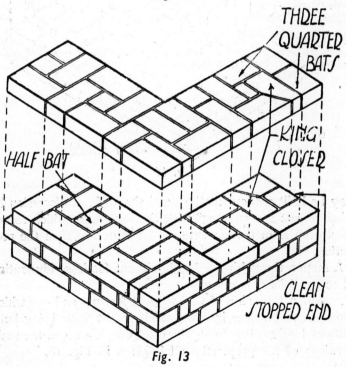

Fig. 13

of a wall should be at least equal to two-thirds of the thickness of a wall at its base.

There should be one course of footings for every half-brick thickness of the wall.

Brickwork for footings should be built in header bond, but in cases where stretchers are necessary it is best to place them in the centre of the wall as shown in the plan (Fig. 8).

Under the provisions of some local building by-laws, walls

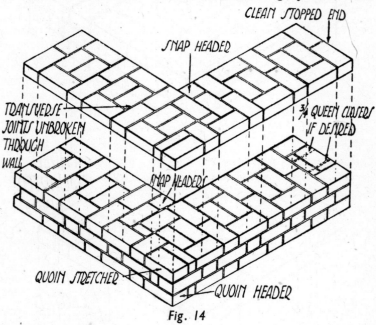

Fig. 14

may be built without footings and the angle of dispersion be taken as not less than 45° with the horizontal, which means the thickness of the concrete must not be less than the projection.

A section through an 18″ wall without footings, illustrating these provisions, is given in Fig. 15.

A section through a 9″ wall without footings and one which conforms to building by-laws which permit walls being built without footings and fulfils the conditions shown in the scale drawings of the proposed Hall is given in Fig. 16.

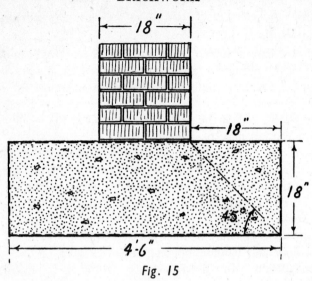

Fig. 15

The section indicates by means of dotted lines the relative spread of brick footings and the thickness of the concrete foundations for a wall of similar thickness.

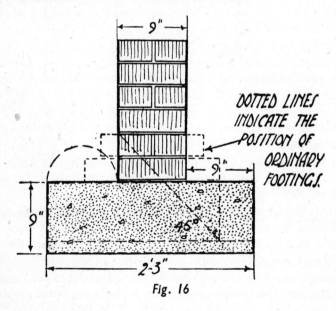

DOTTED LINES INDICATE THE POSITION OF ORDINARY FOOTINGS.

Fig. 16

Brick Walls

Before commencing to build walls reference should be made to the local building by-laws, because their thickness in relation to the height must conform to the requirements of these by-laws.

The setting out of the walls for a portion of the room shown in plan Fig. 49 may be seen in Fig. 1.

Levels are measured from a datum point and these levels will determine the height of floors, roof, etc. Walls may be built entirely in brickwork throughout their height or they may be faced with terra-cotta or stone and backed up with brickwork.

Stone dressings may be incorporated to form special features round door and window openings in brick walls.

Stone Walls.—In districts where stone is plentiful the footings and walls may be built with stone.

Stone-faced Walls.—Wrought stonework is chiefly used in combination with brickwork.

The walls may be said to be built of bricks and faced with stone. For such walls it is important that the heights of the stone courses should be arranged so that they coincide with the heights of the several brick courses.

The facing stones should be properly and effectively bonded with the brickwork and the depth of the stone on the wall being $4\frac{1}{2}''$, $9''$, $13\frac{1}{2}''$ and so on.

Fig. 17 shows the construction at the base of a stone-faced wall with brick backing, together with the construction of the ground floor.

It will be noticed that the width of the concrete foundation under this wall with footings is less than that shown at the base of the wall (Fig. 15).

Brick Quoins are the external angles of walls. They should be square in plan and the measurements for the setting out of door and window openings taken from these quoins. Cross-walls and projections, such as separating walls and fireplace openings, are also set out and squared from the main walls.

External angles, other than right angles, are termed squint

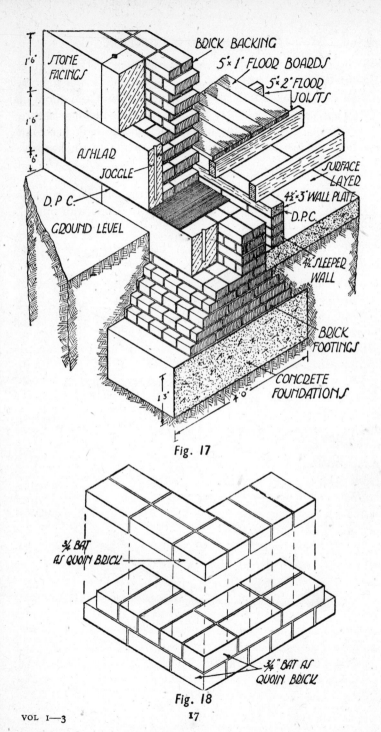

Fig. 17

Fig. 18

quoins. Figs. 9-14 show the arrangement of bricks at the quoin portion of walls built in English and Flemish bonds.

An alternative arrangement for the bricks at the quoin end of two 9″ walls is shown in Fig. 18. In this instance a three-quarter bat is used as the quoin brick in the stretcher course in place of the usual 2¼″ closer next to the quoin header.

Intersecting Walls

When one wall intersects another, the ordinary rules for brickwork hold good with the addition that one wall must be bonded into the other.

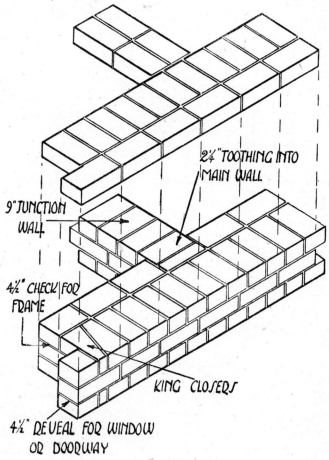

2¼″ TOOTHING INTO MAIN WALL

9″ JUNCTION WALL

4½″ CHECK FOR FRAME

KING CLOSERS

4½″ REVEAL FOR WINDOW OR DOORWAY

Fig. 19

The bond is obtained by opening out the stretching course of the main wall and placing a $2\frac{1}{4}''$ closer in the wall in each alternate course, thereby forming a cavity $2\frac{1}{4}''$ deep for the insertion of the cross-wall, as shown in Figs. 19 and 20.

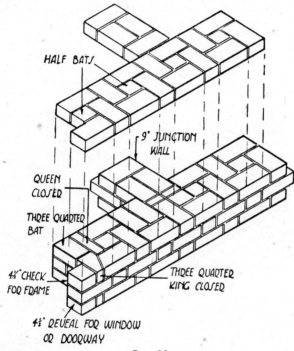

Fig. 20

Brick Piers

These may be built independently as shown in Figs. 21–27, or they may be attached to and form part of a wall as shown in Fig. 28.

The brickwork between two window openings may be referred to as a brick pier.

Window and Door Jambs.—When forming window and door openings in walls provision should be made for the fixing of the window-frame by recessing the jambs to suit the type of frame to be used.

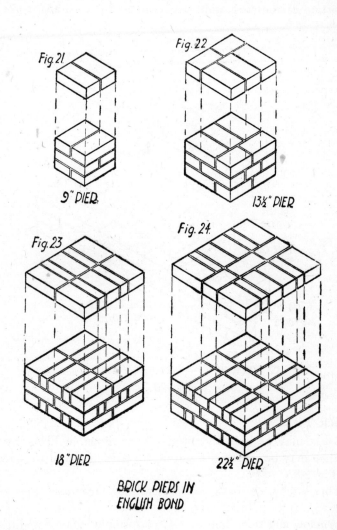

Fig. 21

9" PIER

Fig. 22

13½" PIER

Fig. 23

18" PIER

Fig. 24

22½" PIER

BRICK PIERS IN
ENGLISH BOND

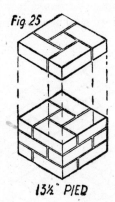

Fig. 25

13½" PIER

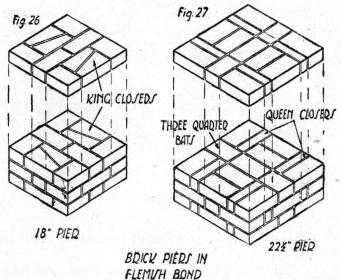

Fig. 26

KING CLOSERS

18" PIER

Fig. 27

THREE QUARTER BATS

QUEEN CLOSERS

22½" PIER

BRICK PIERS IN
FLEMISH BOND

Sometimes a straight-through jamb is desired, in which case the frame is intended to abutt the jamb without recourse to a rebate, as shown in Figs. 143, 144.

The vertical face-work at the sides of an opening is termed the reveal and the bonding is treated in a manner similar to quoins, but a slight variation is needed in setting out for the

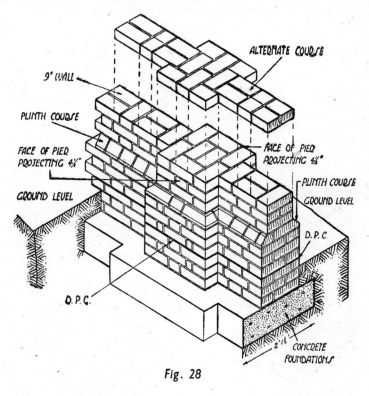

Fig. 28

rebate, the depth of which is governed by the type of window or door frame.

Details showing the arrangement of the bricks for jambs built in English and Flemish bonds are given in Figs. 29–40. Stones comprising the stone dressings at the sides of window or door openings are termed jamb stones, and the recessed portion from the face of a wall to the frame is termed the outside reveal, while the surface which forms the face of the

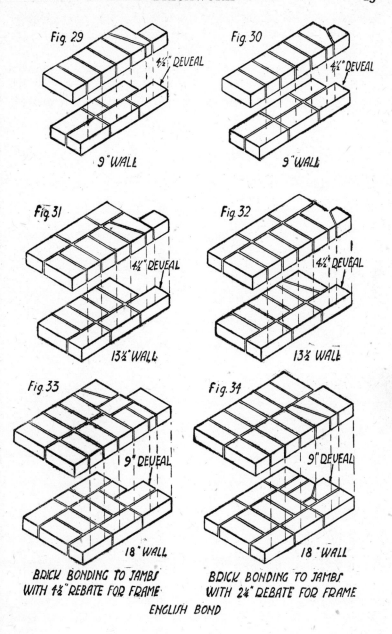

Fig. 29 — 4½" REVEAL — 9" WALL

Fig. 30 — 4½" REVEAL — 9" WALL

Fig. 31 — 4½" REVEAL — 13½" WALL

Fig. 32 — 4½" REVEAL — 13½" WALL

Fig. 33 — 9" REVEAL — 18" WALL

Fig. 34 — 9" REVEAL — 18" WALL

BRICK BONDING TO JAMBS
WITH 4½" REBATE FOR FRAME

BRICK BONDING TO JAMBS
WITH 2¼" REBATE FOR FRAME

ENGLISH BOND

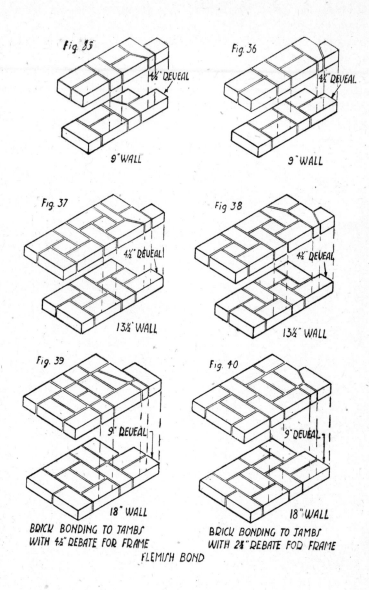

Fig. 35

4½" DEVEAL

9" WALL

Fig. 36

4½" DEVEAL

9" WALL

Fig. 37

4½" DEVEAL

13½" WALL

Fig 38

4½" DEVEAL

13½" WALL

Fig. 39

9" DEVEAL

18" WALL

BRICK BONDING TO JAMBS
WITH 4½" REBATE FOR FRAME

Fig. 40

9" DEVEAL

18" WALL

BRICK BONDING TO JAMBS
WITH 2½" REBATE FOR FRAME

FLEMISH BOND

rebate is termed the inside reveal. A constructional sketch showing the brick bonding for the jambs at the side of the main entrance of the proposed Hall, together with the construction of the entrance steps and vestibule floor, is shown in Fig. 41.

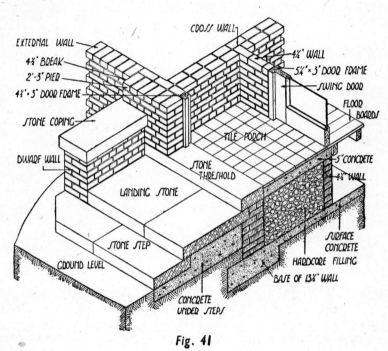

Fig. 41

CHAPTER IV

DAMP-PROOF COURSES

DAMPNESS is always liable to penetrate the bases of walls and ground floors, therefore methods of prevention must be employed in their construction.

Water pressure under basement floors and ground floors may be relieved by placing a system of surface drainage over the whole of the site and under the floors, so that the excessive moisture can be drained away.

There are three methods of damp-proofing walls, floors, etc.

(1) **Membrane damp-proofing**, which consists of incorporating in walls, floors, etc., layers of impervious material such as slates, sheet lead, metallic felts, or mastic asphalt.

(2) **Integral damp-proofing**, in which certain compounds are added to the concrete during the process of mixing. The success of this method depends upon the filling, or the elimination of voids, which renders the material more dense.

(3) **Surface treatment**, in which the surface of walls is treated with a waterproof paint or coated with cement mortar which has been integrally waterproofed.

Damp-proof Courses for Walls

The damp-proof course for the base of an ordinary wall should be situated about 6″ above the ground level, and continue unbroken throughout the entire thickness and length of the wall, irrespective of the changes in the level occasioned by a rising and falling ground level. In the instance of ground floors constructed in timber, the damp-proof course may be continuous through the wall and under the plates upon which the ends of the joists rest.

When walls are built in conjunction with concrete ground floors, the position of the damp-proof course should be level

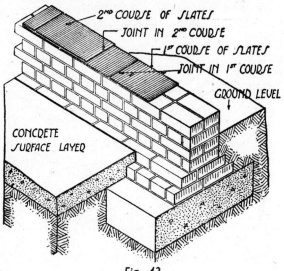

2ND COURSE OF SLATES
JOINT IN 2ND COURSE
1ST COURSE OF SLATES
JOINT IN 1ST COURSE
GROUND LEVEL
CONCRETE SURFACE LAYER

Fig. 42

and continuous with the top of the surface concrete which covers the site.

When slates are used as a damp-proof course they should

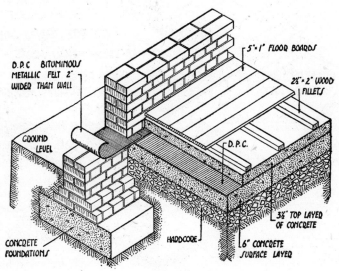

D.P.C BITUMINOUS METALLIC FELT 2" WIDER THAN WALL
5"×1" FLOOR BOARDS
2½"×2" WOOD FILLETS
GROUND LEVEL
D.P.C.
3½" TOP LAYER OF CONCRETE
CONCRETE FOUNDATIONS
HARDCORE
6" CONCRETE SURFACE LAYER

Fig. 43

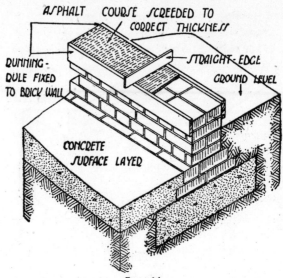

ASPHALT COURSE SCREEDED TO CORRECT THICKNESS

RUNNING-RULE FIXED TO BRICK WALL

STRAIGHT-EDGE

GROUND LEVEL

CONCRETE SURFACE LAYER

Fig. 44

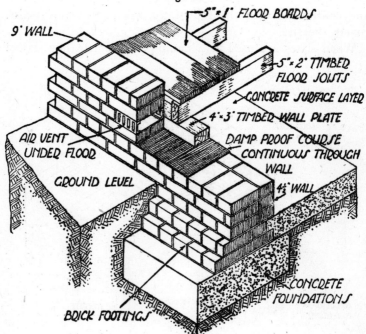

5"×1" FLOOR BOARDS

9" WALL

5"×2" TIMBER FLOOR JOISTS

CONCRETE SURFACE LAYER

4"×3" TIMBER WALL PLATE

AIR VENT UNDER FLOOR

DAMP PROOF COURSE CONTINUOUS THROUGH WALL

GROUND LEVEL

4½" WALL

BRICK FOOTINGS

CONCRETE FOUNDATIONS

Fig. 45

be bedded in cement mortar in two layers and bonded, or lap-jointed, as shown in Fig. 42.

Metallic felt should be laid on a cement mortar bed and the joints in the material lapped as shown in Fig. 43.

Mastic asphalt is an excellent damp-proofing material and when used as a damp-proof course in walls it should be applied in two layers each being screeded as shown in Fig. 44.

When a wall plate rests upon an offset built as part of the base of a wall the asphalt should cover the entire thickness of the wall as shown in Fig. 45.

Damp-proofing Floors

Ground floors situated below the outside ground level may be kept free from dampness by screeding an impervious layer over the whole of the floor area. In certain circumstances it

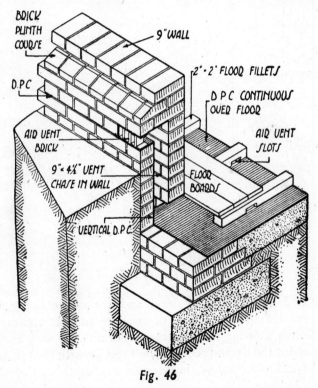

Fig. 46

may be found necessary to continue the damp-proof course through the external wall and extending it vertically to finish in a horizontal joint about 6″ above ground level.

A better method is to form a projecting plinth course at the base of the wall and enclose the vertical asphalt layer within the thickness of the wall as shown in Fig. 46.

Open Areas

When site conditions permit, an open area may be formed in front of external walls, in which case the outside soil is

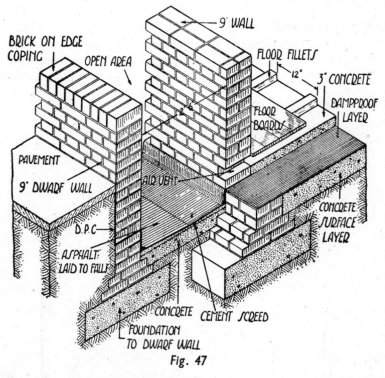

Fig. 47

excavated below the floor level and a small retaining wall built parallel to the face of the wall to support the earth.

A sketch showing the construction of an open area and the position for the damp-proof course, together with the construction of the ground floor, is given in Fig. 47.

Closed Areas

Site conditions will often preclude the construction of an open area.

In such circumstances dampness may be kept from the

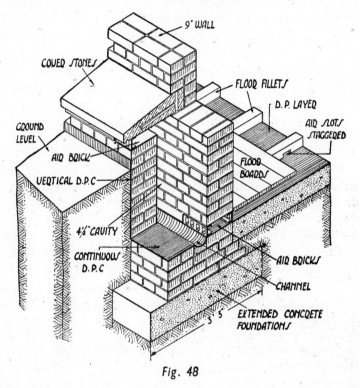

Fig. 48

walls and floors by forming a closed cavity at the base of the wall as shown in Fig. 48.

This method of damp-proofing will assist in keeping the walls dry, but it often fails in its effectiveness because the cavity is liable to become filled with all kinds of dirt and refuse.

CHAPTER V

CONSTRUCTION OF FLOORS

FLOORS may be classified according to their position in a building, or by the materials employed in their construction, viz. :

(1) Basement floors.	(4) Timber floors.
(2) Ground floors.	(5) Concrete floors.
(3) Upper floors.	(6) Hollow block floors.

Floors may also be classified according to the type of beams which support the finishings, whether they are of timber, steel or concrete.

Basement Floors

The most important consideration in the construction of basement floors is the elimination of dampness and dry rot.

Dampness may be excluded by placing rows of land drain pipes under the floor or around the external walls, below the floor level, and connecting the pipes to a land drainage system. A concrete floor slab should be formed on a bed of hard core and then covered with a damp-proofing course formed continuous through the walls and up the vertical external face of the wall to a point above ground level. The floor slab should then be covered with another layer of concrete, which will form the base for the floor finishings.

Concrete Ground Floors

Success in the construction of solid concrete floors depends upon the methods adopted in eliminating dampness and the provision of a system of ventilation under the floor.

The finishings of solid concrete ground floors may be protected from dampness by placing a layer of concrete on top of the damp-proofing layer, thus forming a double floor slab as shown in Fig. 47, and if solid block flooring is desired, the blocks should be laid on a bitumastic mixture, whereas floor-boards should be fixed to wood battens as shown in Figs. 46-8.

If small notches are cut in the bottom portion of the battens and direct contact is made with air ducts formed within the thickness of an external wall and placed in suitable positions, air will be permitted to pass along the spaces between the battens and under the floor-boards, by the provision of these notches.

The floor-boards should not be grooved and tongued or tightly jointed and it is also inadvisable to cover them with thick linoleum.

Fig. 130 shows the construction of a solid ground floor finished with floor tiles.

Timber Ground Floors

The finishings of these floors are supported upon wood joists or beams placed on edge and of sufficient depth to avoid deflection.

The joists should be spaced from 12″ to 14″ apart, centre to centre, and arranged as shown in the plan and section in Figs. 49 and 50.

The joists may be supported by extending the thickness of the wall at its base or by building 9″ square brick piers from the concrete surface layer, at various intervals over the floor area, for the bedding of the wall plates. The piers should be covered with a slate damp-proof course and then surmounted with a piece of 4″ × 3″ timber placed on edge to form a bearing for the support of floor joists, as shown in Fig. 51.

The timber joists should be nailed or cogged to the wall plates.

Sleeper Walls.—Large spans are avoided by building dwarf walls from the surface concrete for the intermediate support of the joists.

The provision of these walls will permit the use of timbers of less depth than would otherwise be required.

5″ × 2″ joists placed 14″ apart centre to centre will be suitable to resist the normal dead and superimposed loads over a span of 7′.

When building sleeper walls, provision should be made for a free current of air to pass under the floor by omitting

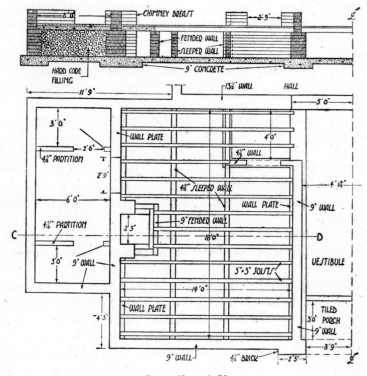

Figs. 49 and 50

bricks at various intervals throughout the length of the walls.

Dampness will be kept from the floor timbers if the wall plates are bedded on a damp-proof course as shown in Fig. 52.

Concrete Surface Layer

A layer of concrete, having a minimum thickness of 4″, must be placed over the whole of the floor area between the walls.

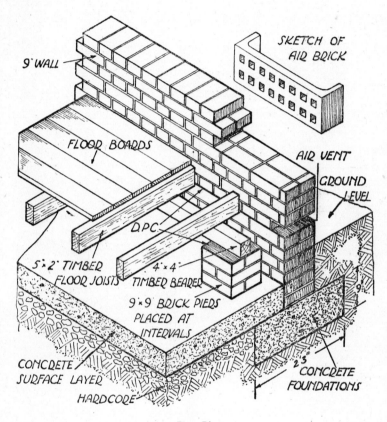

Fig. 51

The provision of this layer is compulsory under local building by-laws.

Fine aggregate Portland cement concrete should be used

for this purpose and the top surface of the concrete rendered dense by being finished with a trowel.

This finishing process will assist in preventing the transference of air from the ground into the room above.

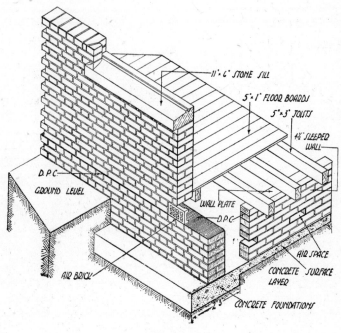

Fig. 52

CHAPTER VI

CONSTRUCTION OF FIREPLACE OPENINGS

A FIREPLACE is formed by building attached brick piers from the internal face of a wall, or by a projection built out from the face of a wall.

The brick piers on each side of the opening are called jambs and the brickwork above the lintol over the opening is called the chimney-breast.

The brickwork projecting from the wall face should be built up from the foundations in a manner similar to attached piers, and where footings are used, they should continue round the projecting brickwork.

Every fireplace should have a separate flue, continuous to the top of the chimney-stack, and no openings for ventilation and other purposes should be made into the flue.

Reference should be made to the regulations as to the construction of chimneys and flues as contained in the local building by-laws.

Fireplaces can be arranged as single projections or placed back to back or across an angle of a room.

Where fireplace openings are situated in a party wall they must have a 9″ chimney-back to a height of 12″ above the mantel, but where they are placed on external or other walls, the chimney-back may be $4\frac{1}{2}″$ thick. The minimum width for the jambs is 9″, but jambs $13\frac{1}{2}″$ wide are commonly adopted.

Flues.—The size of flues must be at least 9″ × 9″ for ordinary grates, but flues conveying smoke from kitchen grates or boilers should be at least $13\frac{1}{2}″$ × 9″. Flues should be enclosed in brick walls $4\frac{1}{2}″$ thick and lined with a layer of Portland cement trowelled to a fine finish, a process which is termed pargetting. The object of pargetting is to fill in any side crevices and produce a surface which will offer little resistance to the ascending smoke.

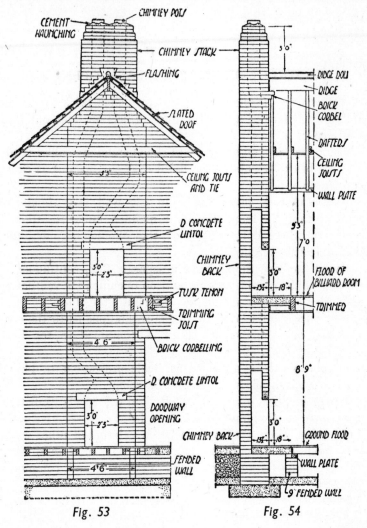

Fig. 53   Fig. 54

The division walls between two or more flues are termed 'withs' and are usually $4\frac{1}{2}''$ wide.

Flues should converge to form a group within a chimney-stack.

Chimney-stacks are often built with $4\frac{1}{2}''$ external walls, but thicker walls should be used when circumstances demand. An elevation and section through the chimney-stack and fireplace openings shown in the scale drawings of the proposed Hall are given in Figs. 53 and 54.

Hearths

To assist in the prevention of an outbreak of fire, the base of a fireplace opening, and for at least 18" in front of the chimney-jambs and 6" beyond the opening, must be constructed with fire-resisting materials. Hearths to fireplaces on ground floors are usually formed of a slab of Portland cement concrete,

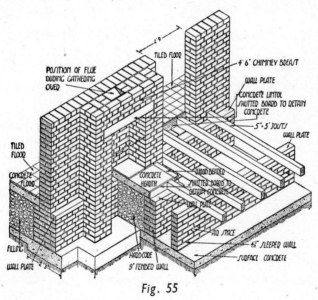

Fig. 55

the front portion being supported on a dwarf wall termed a fender wall and as shown in Fig. 55.

Precast concrete slabs are used occasionally for this purpose.

The front hearths to fireplaces on upper floors were usually supported on a brick trimmer arch, which was built between the face of the chimney breast and the wood trimmer joist, but the modern practice is to form a slab of Portland cement

concrete at the base of the fireplace opening, the front portion
of the slab being supported on the trimmer joist, as shown in
Fig. 56. The converging of the flues to form a chimney-stack

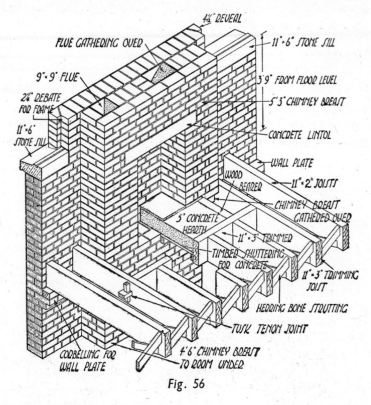

Fig. 56

usually occurs in the space between the ceiling joists and the
roof rafters, and the corbelling out of the chimney-breast for
the accommodation of the flues occurs within the thickness
of the floors as shown in Fig. 53.

CHAPTER VII

ARCHES

THE object of an arch is to carry weight over an opening and to transmit this weight to the supports or abutments.

Whether constructed of brick or stone, an arch consists of a mechanical arrangement of wedge-shaped units, or wedge-shaped joints between the units and built about some form of curve.

The units support each other by the mutual pressure of their own weight and the structure maintains its position by the resistance of the supports or abutments.

The chief terms connected with arches are :

Intrados or soffit is the under-surface of an arch.

Extrados is the outer surface or upper curve of an arch.

Springing line is the imaginary straight line joining the two springing points.

Crown is the highest part in an arch.

Face is the portion of an arch which is in the same plane as the face of the wall.

Voussoirs or archstones are the wedge-shaped units which comprise the arch.

Springing stone is the first voussoir at springing level on either side of a stone arch.

Keystone is the wedge-shaped unit at the centre or crown of an arch and one which ' keys ' the other units.

Skewback is the surface between the first voussoir in a flat or segmental arch and the abutment.

Span is the clear horizontal distance between the supports.

Rise is the perpendicular height from the springing line to the highest point on the intrados.

Abutments are the masses of walling material from which

the arch springs and which receives the thrust transmitted by the arch.

Arch forms.—Arches are usually named according to the form of the arch-curve or soffit line, such as :

Flat or straight arches in which the soffit and extrados are

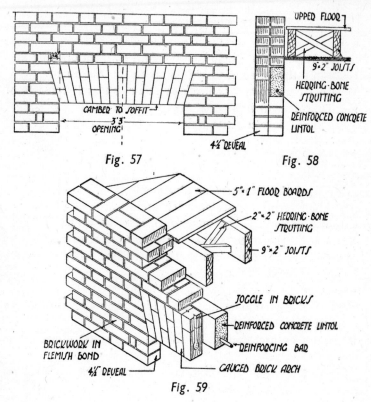

Fig. 57

Fig. 58

Fig. 59

both straight lines and between which imaginary arch curves are presumed to exist.

In brickwork these arches are termed cambered arches, the extrados being straight and the soffit slightly curved. The construction of a brick cambered arch may be seen in Figs. 57, 58 and 59.

Semi-circular arch is one which has its striking centre on the springing line.

Details of a semi-circular axed brick facing arch together with a semi-circular internal two-ring rough brick arch are given in Figs. 60, 61 and 62.

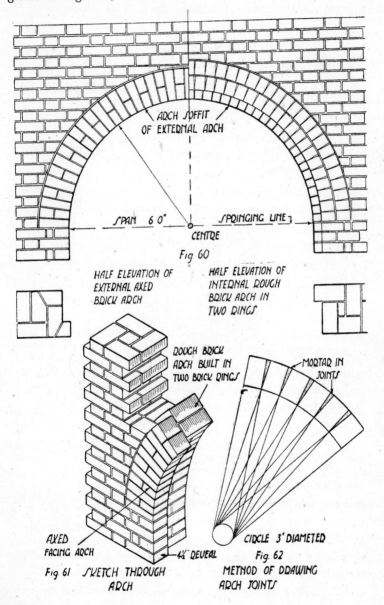

ARCH SOFFIT OF EXTERNAL ARCH

SPAN 6 0"

SPRINGING LINE

CENTRE

Fig 60

HALF ELEVATION OF EXTERNAL AXED BRICK ARCH

HALF ELEVATION OF INTERNAL ROUGH BRICK ARCH IN TWO RINGS

ROUGH BRICK ARCH BUILT IN TWO BRICK RINGS

MORTAR IN JOINTS

AXED FACING ARCH

4½" REVEAL

CIRCLE 3" DIAMETER

Fig. 62

METHOD OF DRAWING ARCH JOINTS

Fig 61 SKETCH THROUGH ARCH

Segmental arch is one which has its striking centre below the springing line. An external and internal elevation of a gauged brick segmental arch is given in Fig. 63, and a sketch showing the construction through the arch is given in Fig. 64.

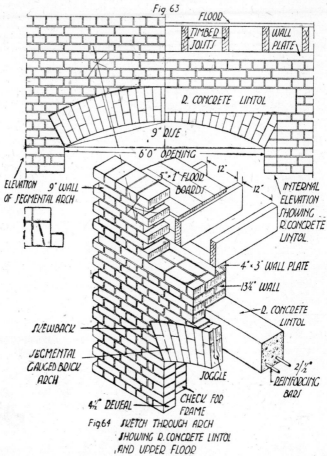

Fig 63

FLOOR

TIMBER JOISTS

WALL PLATE

R. CONCRETE LINTOL

9" RISE

6'0" OPENING

5"×1" FLOOR BOARDS

12"

12"

ELEVATION 9" WALL OF SEGMENTAL ARCH

INTERNAL ELEVATION SHOWING R. CONCRETE LINTOL.

4"×3" WALL PLATE

13½" WALL

R. CONCRETE LINTOL

SKEWBACK

SEGMENTAL GAUGED BRICK ARCH

JOGGLE

2/½" REINFORCING BARS

4½" REVEAL

CHECK FOR FRAME

Fig 64   SKETCH THROUGH ARCH SHOWING R. CONCRETE LINTOL AND UPPER FLOOR

Semi-elliptical arch is one in which the arch curve is trammelled in the form of an ellipse; but when built in brickwork the curve is usually struck from three or five centres in which case the arch line is an approximate elliptical curve.

Pointed arches are those which have a pointed crown, the curves being struck from two or four centres

Brick Soldier Arches.—The modern tendency is to substitute soldier arches for cambered arches. The arch is formed by placing the bricks side by side with their lengths vertical. As the units are not wedge-shaped they should be supported upon

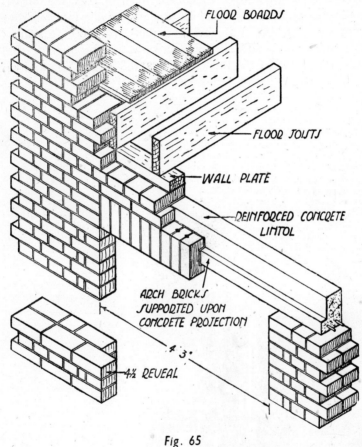

FLOOR BOARDS

FLOOR JOISTS

WALL PLATE

REINFORCED CONCRETE LINTOL

ARCH BRICKS SUPPORTED UPON CONCRETE PROJECTION

4' 3"

4½ REVEAL

Fig. 65

a reinforced concrete lintol as shown in Fig. 65 or upon an L-iron as shown in Fig. 103.

Brick arches may be classified as follows :

Rough arches are those which are built with ordinary bricks. The bricks are not cut wedge-shape, consequently the joints are wider at the extrados than at the intrados, therefore they are usually built in half brick rings or in heading bond as shown in Fig. 60. The method for obtaining the wedge-shaped joint lines is given in Fig. 62.

Axed arches are those in which the bricks are roughly cut wedge-shape ; details of which are given in Figs. 60 and 61.

Gauged arches are those in which specially made bricks, known as 'rubbers,' are cut or rubbed to accurate shapes. The units are bedded in lime putty which produces a thin joint line between the bricks as indicated in Figs. 63 and 64.

CHAPTER VIII

TIMBER CENTERS

THE shaped timber frames which are used for the temporary support of arches during their construction are known as centers and they are framed in a manner similar to a timber roof truss.

Arch centers differ in construction according to the materials of which the arch is constructed, length of span, depth of soffit and form of arch curve.

As weight will be thrown on the center while the arch is being built, it should be constructed and erected so that it will resist the strains at all points.

All centers should be supported on folding wedges which should be placed at the top of the props or uprights and immediately under the center.

The inclusion of folding wedges will assist in the easing and striking of the center after the arch has been completed and the surrounding walling built up to resist the thrust.

Centers for brick arches should follow the correct line of the arch curve with the laggings placed fairly close together so that the arch bricks may be placed direct on to the top of the laggings, as shown in Fig. 66.

Centers for Stone Arches

When the voussoirs of a stone arch are shaped to bond with the surrounding ashlar courses, the wood centers should be made to a smaller radius than the arch curve so that folding wedges may be placed on top of the laggings, as shown in Fig. 66.

This procedure is recommended because arch-stones usually require a certain amount of adjustment during fixing processes.

The laggings should be placed to allow each voussoir to rest upon two pairs of folding wedges.

It is preferable to construct the center with its lower edge

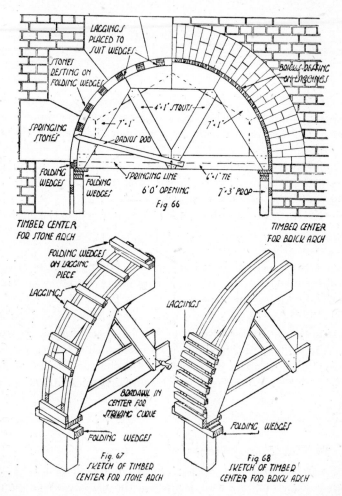

TIMBER CENTER
FOR STONE ARCH

TIMBER CENTER
FOR BRICK ARCH

a few inches below springing line so that folding wedges may be placed at the ends of the centers and between the jambs.

Sketches of timber centers for brick and stone semi-circular arches are given in Figs. 67 and 68.

Centers for the support of pointed arches and stone arches

with concentric arch curves should follow the correct line of the arch so that the arch-stones may be placed direct upon the laggings.

Turning Pieces

These are used for the support of brick arches which have a small rise. They may be cut from a single piece of timber,

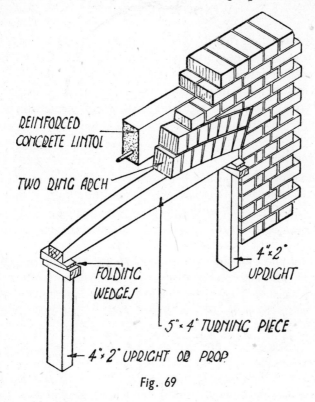

REINFORCED CONCRETE LINTOL

TWO RING ARCH

FOLDING WEDGES

4"×2" UPRIGHT

5"×4" TURNING PIECE

4"×2" UPRIGHT OR PROP

Fig. 69

but if the soffit of the arch is deep, two or more pieces of timber, covered with close laggings, will be necessary.

A sketch showing the construction of a two-ring brick arch being temporarily supported on a turning piece is given in Fig. 69.

CHAPTER IX

WINDOW OPENINGS

THE construction round window openings should be such that dampness is prevented from passing to the interior of a building.

If window-frames are constructed in a proper manner they will assist in preventing damp penetration, but a great deal will depend upon the design and construction of the wall which surrounds the opening.

Window-sills

A window-sill is the member at the base of a window opening ; its main object is to throw off the rainwater and to form a covering to the wall at the base of the opening.

Sills may be formed in various materials, such as stone, brick, tiles and hard-wood.

To become effective it is necessary for the sill to project from the wall face, the projecting portion being provided with a drip, which is formed by cutting a throat in the projecting under surface, or by tilting the material which forms the sill into an inclined position as may be seen in Figs. 139 and 140.

Stone window-sills are usually made longer than the opening, the ends being built into the wall, and horizontal seatings, termed stoolings, are formed for the jambs to rest upon.

These stoolings should not be too long as this may cause the sill to fracture should any settlement occur in the walls, due to superimposed loads.

When a stone window-sill spans an opening in one piece, only the portion of the sill under the jambs should be bedded in mortar, the space between being left free from mortar, so that any unequal settlement which might take place in the wall will not cause the sill to fracture.

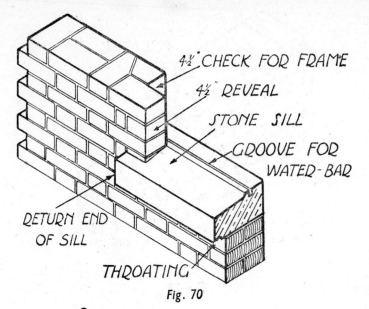

4½" CHECK FOR FRAME

4½" REVEAL

STONE SILL

GROOVE FOR WATER-BAR

RETURN END OF SILL

THROATING

Fig. 70

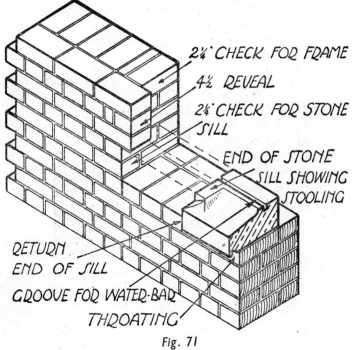

2¼" CHECK FOR FRAME

4½" REVEAL

2¼" CHECK FOR STONE SILL

END OF STONE SILL SHOWING STOOLING

RETURN END OF SILL

GROOVE FOR WATER-BAR

THROATING

Fig. 71

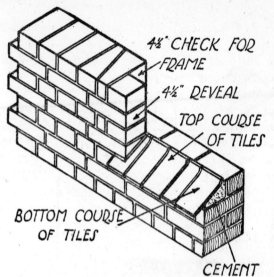

4⅛" CHECK FOR FRAME

4½" REVEAL

TOP COURSE OF TILES

BOTTOM COURSE OF TILES

CEMENT

Fig. 72

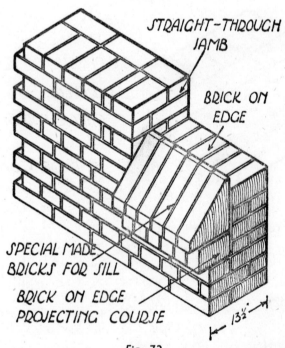

STRAIGHT-THROUGH JAMB

BRICK ON EDGE

SPECIAL MADE BRICKS FOR SILL

BRICK ON EDGE PROJECTING COURSE

13½"

Fig. 73

The open bed joint should be pointed when the construction of the building is complete.

Stone sills may be bedded solid if they comprise more than one stone or they may be point-bedded under mullions. Constructional sketches showing the position and details of stone sills in a brick wall are given in Figs. 70 and 71. When a hard-wood sill surmounts a stone sill, a metal water-bar should be included in the construction.

The inclusion of a water-bar will necessitate the provision of a groove in the top surface of the stone sill and situated about $\frac{3}{4}''$ behind the weathering line. The top exposed surface of the sill should be worked into an inclined surface, which is known as a weathering, and the ends of the weathering finished to the reveals to form the stoolings. The inclusion of metal window-frames necessitates a slight modification in the section of a stone sill.

A groove for a water-bar is not required, but a projection may be formed in the upper portion of the sill over which the sill of the metal window-frame is fitted, as shown in Fig. 143, or the lower portion of the metal frame may be fitted into a rebate cut in the top surface of the sill.

Window-sills add considerably to the appearance of a building, therefore they should be designed in keeping with the style of a building and constructed with appropriate materials.

Bricks and tiles are excellent materials for this purpose, providing the construction will enable them to fulfil the purpose for which they were intended.

Figs. 72 and 73 are details of brick and tile window-sills.

Reinforced Concrete Lintols

It is usual to place a reinforced concrete lintol behind an external lintol or arch in preference to constructing a rough relieving arch in brickwork.

Reinforced concrete lintols may be precast and erected in a monolithic form or they may be cast *in situ*, the latter procedure being preferable when a lintol is intended to span a wide opening. The steel reinforcement should be sufficient to resist the tensional stresses occasioned by the loads which are likely to be transmitted from the floors and roof.

To accomplish this the reinforcement should be placed in the lower portion of the lintol where the tensional stresses occur and the steel bars hooked at each end to assist in maintaining adhesion between the concrete and the steel.

Constructional details through the top portion of window openings showing the inclusion of reinforced concrete lintols are given in Figs. 59, 64 and 65.

CHAPTER X

MASONRY

WROUGHT stonework is used chiefly in combination with brick walls.

Such walls are in reality built of bricks and faced with stonework and are termed stone-faced walls.

Rubble Walls

Walls built with rough uncut stone are called rubble walls. Whereas in walls built of brick and wrought stone facings the strength depends almost entirely upon the manner in which the materials are bonded together, in rubble walls the strength depends very largely upon the mortar between the stones.

For carrying the same loads, rubble walls should be built thicker than walls built of brick and wrought stone.

The appearance and finish of wrought stone walls are predetermined by the shape and dressing of the stones, whereas in rubble walls the resulting appearance depends upon the skill of the walling mason who builds the wall, because the arrangement and bonding of the stones are left to the craftsman.

Rubble walls are generally arranged to fill in between wrought stone quoins and dressings.

Coursed Rubble Walls

The stones are selected for size and roughly worked to course height as shown in Fig. 74.

Random Rubble Walls

The stones are placed in the wall in the condition in which they come from the quarry or they may be roughly squared with the hammer ; the horizontal coursing not being studied.

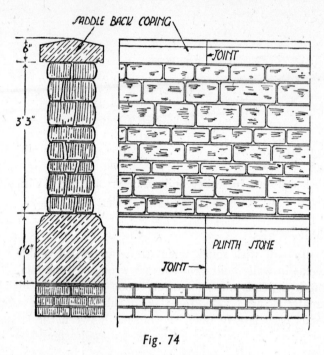

Fig. 74

Random Rubble built to Courses

Stones of irregular height are placed in the wall so that they level up to a horizontal bed at intervals as shown in Fig. 75.

Snecked Rubble Walls

Small rectangular filling stones are inserted at intervals throughout the wall to equalise the varying heights of the adjoining stones (see Fig. 78). Sometimes the stones of these walls have roughly chiselled faces.

Stone Dressings

Face is the term applied to the exposed surface of a stone and is usually the vertical face in elevation. The surface is finished according to the detail or form required.

Return face is the vertical face exposed to the side elevation.

Beds are the lower surfaces upon which the stone rests and

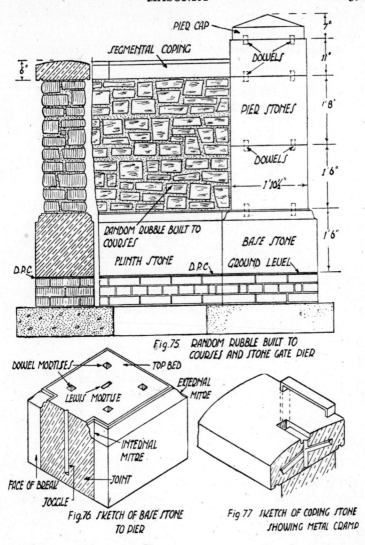

Fig. 75   RANDOM RUBBLE BUILT TO
COURSES AND STONE GATE PIER

Fig. 76   SKETCH OF BASE STONE
TO PIER

Fig 77   SKETCH OF COPING STONE
SHOWING METAL CRAMP

the upper surfaces which support the stones immediately
above. They may be placed horizontal or inclined.

Joints are the surfaces prepared to receive other surfaces
abutting against them.

Quoin stones are the stones placed at an external angle of a building and arranged to bond with the other stones in the wall in each direction.

Ashlar is the term used for finely dressed stone which is

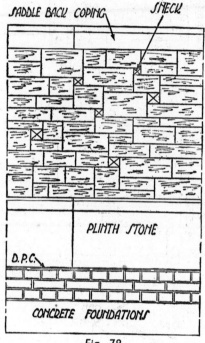

Fig. 78

worked to fit in the general face of the wall. It may be ' plain,' ' rusticated,' ' rock-faced ' or ' chisel-drafted.' A sketch showing the construction of a rusticated ashlar jamb for a window or door opening is given in Fig. 79.

Masonry Joints

Butt-joints are formed by two plane surfaces being butted or placed together. A V-shaped groove, termed a joggle, is cut in the surface of each stone to form a cavity and into which cement grout is poured.

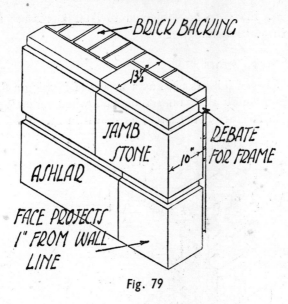

BRICK BACKING

13½"

JAMB
STONE

ASHLAR

10"

REBATE
FOR FRAME

FACE PROJECTS
1" FROM WALL
LINE

Fig. 79

Dowelled Joints

The beds and joints of stone mullions, gate piers, and balustrades are often subjected to lateral pressure, therefore they should be strengthened by the insertion of a metal or slate dowel, half of the dowel being let into the mortise cut in the surface of each stone.

Dowels should not be too long, and when slate is used for this purpose, their length should not exceed twice the width of the cross-section.

A sketch of the base stone for the gate pier, showing the dowel mortises cut in the bed of the stone, is given in Fig. 76.

Cramped Joints

The purpose of a cramp when inserted in stonework is to draw the abutting joint surfaces together, therefore the cramp should fit tightly by being tapped into position and the mortise cut to a depth which will allow room for a cement covering as shown in Fig. 77. Metal cramps are most commonly used, but slate cramps are used when occasion arises.

Mortise and tenon joints are used sometimes in stones

which are likely to be subjected to lateral pressure and for joints in stone landings.

Secret Key Joints

This form of joint is used as a means of forming a flat arch comprising more than one stone and when radiating joints on the surface are not desired, as shown in Fig. 80.

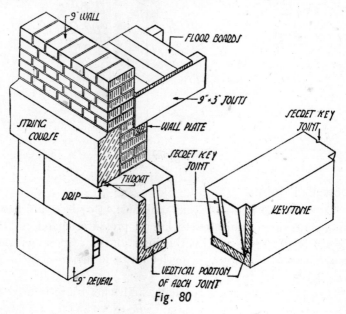

Fig. 80

Stone Copings

Copings are placed on the top of walls to prevent water soaking into the walls from the top surface. They are usually designed to suit the style of architecture of the building, therefore they are of varying sections.

They should project beyond the wall surfaces and be provided with grooves cut in the underside of the projecting portion, thus forming a drip which will assist in throwing the water clear of the surface of the wall. The usual types of stone copings are :

Weathered copings as in Fig. 154.

Saddle-back copings as in Fig. 74.

Segmental copings as in Fig. 75.

The stones should be cramped together by means of a metal cramp inserted across the joints as shown in Fig. 77.

Walls at gable ends should be covered with some form of coping, and when stone is used for this purpose the construction

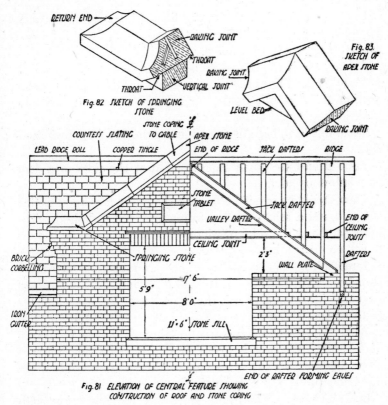

Fig. 82 SKETCH OF SPRINGING STONE

Fig. 83. SKETCH OF APEX STONE

Fig. 81 ELEVATION OF CENTRAL FEATURE SHOWING CONSTRUCTION OF ROOF AND STONE COPING

comprises a springer stone, often in combination with a skew corbel, an apex stone and coping stones. Fig. 81 is an elevation of a gable wall finished with a stone coping and is a detail of the central feature of the main elevation of the proposed Hall. A sketch of the springing stone is given in Fig. 82. For large gables, kneeler stones should be placed about midway between the springer stones and the top of the gable and bonded into the wall so as to resist the thrust of the inclined stonework. The gable should be surmounted by a solid stone, termed an apex stone, which will form the finish to the gable stonework.

A sketch of an apex stone is given in Fig. 83.

MASON'S MITRE

In constructional masonry, the line of intersection between two planes or mouldings is cut in the solid stone and is termed an internal or external mitre.

Ashlar-stop is the intersection of a moulding with an ashlar face and is usually worked in the solid stone, but if the ashlar portion of the stop is worked as a separate stone it should be back-jointed against the return moulding.

Stone sills have been described under the heading of window-sills.

Jamb stones are quoin stones placed at the sides of a door or window opening.

They should be bonded alternatively on the face and through the wall and a rebate for the frame provided if desired. The lower jambs at the sides of window openings should be bedded direct on to the horizontal stoolings of the sill.

Jamb-stops.—The mouldings round an opening are often stopped above the sill or threshold level and various forms of stops are introduced to suit the character of the work and the taste of the designer.

A sketch showing the construction through the main entrance of the proposed Hall is given in Fig. 84. In this instance stone dressings are introduced as an alternative finish and the moulding round the opening is shown stopped.

Stone Arches.—The terms employed in connection with stone arches are similar to those already detailed in the notes on brick arches.

Stone lintols are often employed instead of arches for spanning openings and they should be designed to carry the loads to be placed upon them.

When an opening is spanned by one piece of stone the lintol is termed a 'stone head,' but a number of stones may be employed for this purpose, in which case the 'head' becomes a 'flat-arch' and the joints are made to converge to a centre, as shown in Figs. 85 and 86. Vertical joints may be maintained on the face by forming secret key joints as shown in Fig. 80. A drip should be incorporated in the design of a stone lintol when it is intended to span the external portion of a

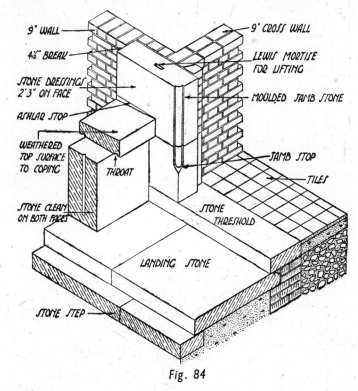

9° WALL
4½° BREAK
STONE DRESSINGS 2'3" ON FACE
ASHLAR STOP
WEATHERED TOP SURFACE TO COPING
THROAT
STONE CLEAN ON BOTH FACES
9° CROSS WALL
LEWIS MORTISE FOR LIFTING
MOULDED JAMB STONE
JAMB STOP
TILES
STONE THRESHOLD
LANDING STONE
STONE STEP

Fig. 84

window or door opening, and flat arches in brickwork should be covered with a lead drip or a projecting course of tiles.

The inclusion of these details will assist in preventing the transmission of moisture to the interior of a building. Fig. 87 is the elevation of a semi-circular stone arch showing alternative methods for the bonding of the arch stones with brick courses and with an ashlar-faced wall.

The elevation of a semi-elliptical stone arch together with a

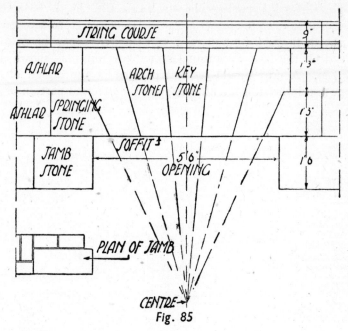

Fig. 85

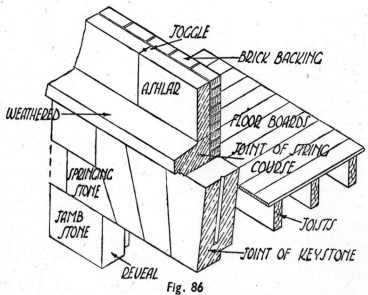

Fig. 86

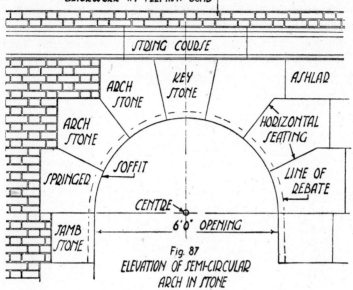

BRICKWORK IN FLEMISH BOND

STRING COURSE

ARCH STONE

KEY STONE

ASHLAR

ARCH STONE

HORIZONTAL SEATING

SOFFIT

SPRINGER

LINE OF REBATE

CENTRE

6'0" OPENING

JAMB STONE

Fig. 87
ELEVATION OF SEMI-CIRCULAR
ARCH IN STONE

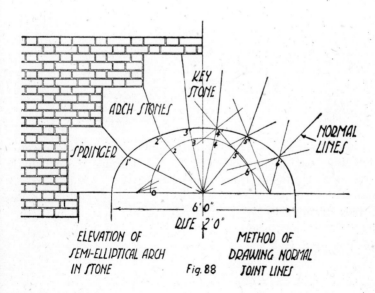

KEY STONE

ARCH STONES

NORMAL LINES

SPRINGER

6'0"

RISE 2'0"

ELEVATION OF
SEMI-ELLIPTICAL ARCH
IN STONE

METHOD OF
DRAWING NORMAL
JOINT LINES

Fig. 88

method for obtaining the best position for the joint lines and the geometrical method for drawing the joint lines normal to the curve is given in Fig. 88.

Whereas in brickwork an approximate elliptical arch curve is usually adopted because of economy in cutting, in masonry the true elliptical curve is usually preferred.

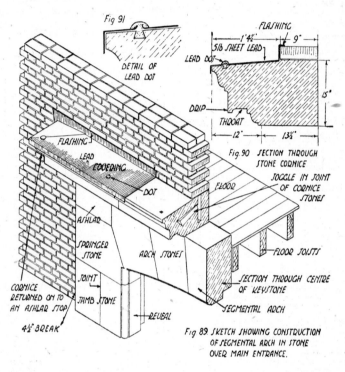

Fig 91

DETAIL OF LEAD DOT

FLASHING
5lb SHEET LEAD
LEAD DOT
1'4½"   9"

DRIP
THROAT
12"   13½"
15"

Fig. 90 SECTION THROUGH STONE CORNICE

FLASHING
LEAD
FLASHING
DOT
FLOOR

JOGGLE IN JOINT OF CORNICE STONES

ASHLAR
SPRINGER STONE
ARCH STONES
JOINT
CORNICE RETURNED ON TO AN ASHLAR STOP
JAMB STONE
REVEAL
4½" BREAK

FLOOR JOISTS

SECTION THROUGH CENTRE OF KEYSTONE
SEGMENTAL ARCH

Fig 89 SKETCH SHOWING CONSTRUCTION OF SEGMENTAL ARCH IN STONE OVER MAIN ENTRANCE.

Figs. 89, 90 and 91 is a sketch and details showing the construction over the main entrance and includes a segmental stone arch springing from stone jambs, the arch being surmounted by a stone cornice.

This example is given as an alternative suggestion to the details of the main entrance shown on the scale drawings of the proposed Hall.

CHAPTER XI

MASONRY (*continued*)

Stone Cornices

THE term cornice is usually applied to the projecting course which crowns that part of the building to which it is affixed.

One important function of a cornice is to protect the surface of the wall from moisture, therefore it should be designed to carry out this purpose effectively.

Provision should be made for the proper discharge of rain-water from the top projecting surface of the cornice and a continuous drip included in the profile of the cornice and placed as near to the nosing as the detail will allow.

A cornice may be complete in one stone, as shown in Figs. 89–93, or they may be built up in a series of courses, each assisting in supporting the projecting portion of the course immediately above.

When a stone cornice is situated at the top of a wall its stability is often maintained by placing a heavy course of stones or other walling material above the cornice. This course of stone is known as a blocking course, the top surface of which is usually worked inclined. It is advisable to strengthen this course by inserting a metal cramp across the joints between the stones.

Details of a main cornice are given in Figs. 92 and 94. Steel-work plays a very important part in the construction of stone cornices and in the manner of jointing, bedding and fixing the stones, but this type of construction will be dealt with in a later volume.

Coverings to Cornices.—The exposed top surfaces of cornices should be weathered or worked inclined towards the nosing or the wall face.

If the top surface is worked towards the wall face, a channel may be provided to carry off the rainwater from the top surface, the bottom of the channel being inclined towards outlets for the discharge of the rainwater into a rainwater head as shown in Figs. 92 and 93.

The whole of the top surface of the cornice including the channel should be covered with an impervious material such as sheet lead or asphalt.

When sheet lead is used the back edge of the sheet should be turned into a flashing groove cut in the vertical face of the stonework which is immediately above the cornice, and the front edge turned down over the nosing of the cornice and finished about $\frac{1}{4}''$ below the bottom arris of the nosing, to form a drip.

To prevent the lead being lifted by the wind, etc., dovetailed dot holes are cut in the top surface of the cornice, close to the nosing, and these are filled with molten lead, the casting process leaving a raised projection on the top surface of the lead as shown in Figs. 89–91.

When asphalt is used for covering a cornice, it should be spread over the surface in two layers and secured along the front edge by being keyed into a dovetailed groove provided in the stonework.

A drip may be formed by introducing a strip of sheet lead which is turned into a dovetailed groove and dressed over the nosing to form a drip.

A detail showing the finish of the asphalt and the lead drip is shown in Figs. 92–4.

String courses are the horizontal bands of stonework projecting from the face of the wall.

They are usually moulded and placed in positions which will accentuate the horizontal divisions of a building. Sometimes they are in the form of a plain face projecting a few inches from the face of the wall, the top surface being weathered. A drip may be formed by cutting a groove in the bottom portion of the projecting stonework as shown in Fig. 80.

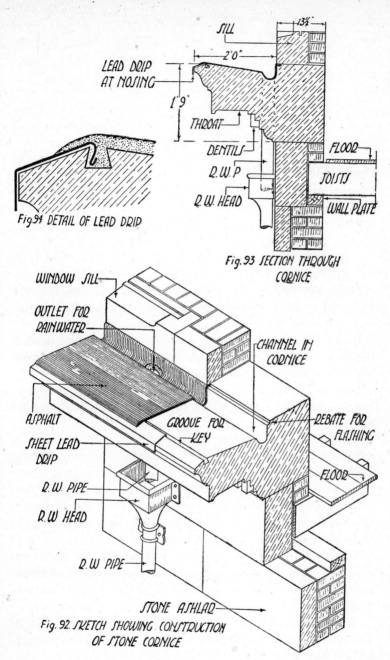

SILL

13½"

LEAD DRIP
AT NOSING

2'0"

1'9"

THROAT

DENTILS

R.W.P

R.W. HEAD

FLOOR

JOISTS

WALL PLATE

Fig.94 DETAIL OF LEAD DRIP

Fig.93 SECTION THROUGH
CORNICE

WINDOW SILL

OUTLET FOR
RAINWATER

CHANNEL IN
CORNICE

ASPHALT

GROOVE FOR
KEY

REBATE FOR
FLASHING

SHEET LEAD
DRIP

FLOOR

R.W. PIPE

R.W. HEAD

R.W. PIPE

STONE ASHLAR

Fig. 92. SKETCH SHOWING CONSTRUCTION
OF STONE CORNICE

CHAPTER XII

CARPENTRY

Upper Floor Construction

TIMBER upper floors consist of boards supported on timber beams or joists.

There are three types of timber upper floors, viz. :
   (1) Single floors.
   (2) Double floors.
   (3) Framed floors.

Single Floors.—In this type of floor construction, common or bridging joists span the whole distance from wall to wall and rest upon wall plates.

Double Floors.—The joists are supported on intermediate beams of steel or timber and the floor area is divided into bays which are bridged by common joists.

Framed Floors.—The joists are supported on secondary beams of steel or timber which in turn are supported on main beams.

Timber Ground Floors.—Light timber joists are laid in whichever direction is most convenient and the ends of the joists are supported on wall plates which are bedded on the brick walls and as shown in Figs. 49 and 50.

To reduce the length of span and to economise in timber, intermediate supports are built at convenient intervals from 6' to 8' apart across the floor area.

These intermediate supports are termed sleeper walls, and they are built up from the concrete surface layer and surmounted with a timber wall plate bedded on a damp-proof course.

When the joists run in the direction as shown in Fig. 50 the joists in front of fireplace openings are carried on a 9″ fender wall as shown in Fig. 55.

TIMBER UPPER FLOORS

For the construction of ground floors, the concrete surface layer affords a convenient means of providing intermediate support to the floor joists, but in upper floor construction this procedure is impossible.

The safe limit of span for single floors is 16 to 18 ft. The sizes for the joists are usually fixed by local building bye-laws, but in special circumstances these sizes should be obtained by calculation.

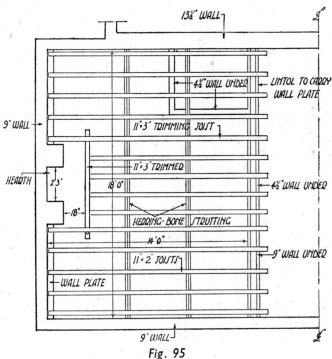

Fig. 95

The joists should be spaced from 12″ to 14″ apart, centre to centre, with at least 4″ bearing on the wall plates.

In best-quality work the wall plates are cogged to the joists, but the more usual practice is to secure the joists to the wall plate by means of skew nailing. A plan showing the spacing for the timber joists for a portion of an upper floor is given in Fig. 95.

Trimming.—Openings for stairs, chimney-breasts, lifts, etc., have to be provided in upper floors, and the joists which are interrupted for this purpose are supported by heavier timbers termed trimmers or trimming joists running at right angles to the common or bridging joists.

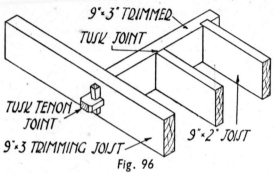

Fig. 96

Trimmers should be 1″ thicker than the common joists and the trimming joists ½″ thicker for every joist trimmed into them.

The trimmer is often framed into the trimming joists by means of a tusk tenon joint.

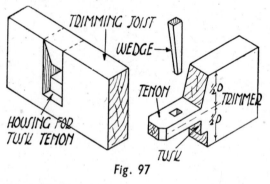

Fig. 97

The tenon is made to pass through the trimming joist, and projects far enough to enable a wedge to be driven through a mortise which is cut in the tenon.

By driving the wedge in position, the shoulders of the joint are brought up tight, thereby making a rigid joint.

Details of a tusk tenon joint are given in Figs. 96 and 97.

A similar joint is often used between the trimmer and trimmed joists, but in this case the tenon does not project beyond the face of the trimmer.

A detail of the joint is given in Fig. 98.

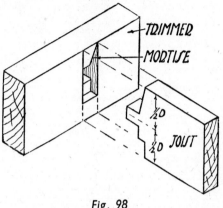

Fig. 98

A bevelled and housed joint may be used for connecting the trimmer and trimmed joists. A detail of which is given in Fig. 99.

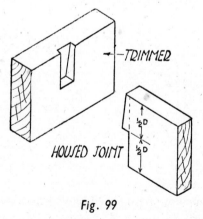

Fig. 99

A metal stirrup is used sometimes instead of a tusk tenon joint. It is a cheaper form of construction and may be used with advantage in certain circumstances.

A detail of a metal stirrup is given in Fig. 100.

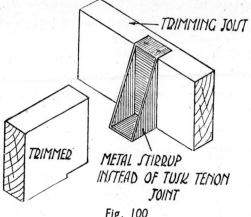

Fig. 100

Strutting.—The joists of upper floors should be stiffened by inserting a row, or a series of rows, of herring-bone strutting across the centre of the floor, or at about 5' intervals in large spans.

The strutting is formed by nailing small pieces of timber between each joist and crossing them from the top to the bottom edges of the joists in a continuous line across the floor,

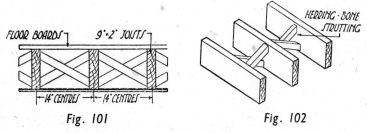

Fig. 101   Fig. 102

the outer joists being wedged against the walls. Details of herring-bone strutting may be seen in Figs. 101–3.

Solid strutting is sometimes employed for the same purpose, but is not considered so effective owing to the possible warping and twisting of the joists.

Wall plates should be continuous throughout the length of the walls and where joints occur they should be halved.

They are best kept clear of the wall faces and supported

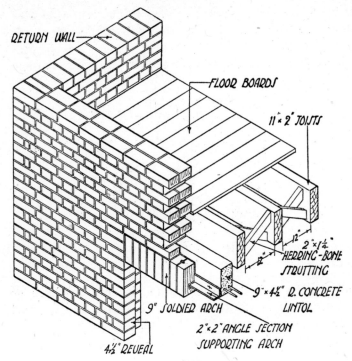

RETURN WALL

FLOOR BOARDS

11" × 2" JOISTS

12"

2" × 1¼"
HERRING-BONE
STRUTTING

9" × 4½" R. CONCRETE
LINTOL

9" SOLDIER ARCH

2" × 2" ANGLE SECTION
SUPPORTING ARCH

4½" REVEAL

Fig. 103

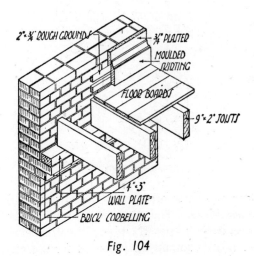

2" × ¾" ROUGH GROUNDS

¾" PLASTER

MOULDED
SKIRTING

FLOOR BOARDS

9" × 2" JOISTS

4" × 3"
WALL PLATE

BRICK CORBELLING

Fig. 104

on brick corbelling courses as shown in Fig. 104, or bedded on offsets formed by the varying thickness of the wall as shown in Fig. 105.

Wall plates and the ends of timber joists are occasionally

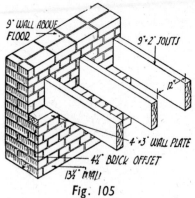

9" WALL ABOVE FLOOR
9"×2" JOISTS
12"
4"×3" WALL PLATE
4½" BRICK OFFSET
13½" WALL

Fig. 105

built in the wall, but this method is not considered good practice, because the timber which is enclosed in the wall is liable to become affected by dry rot.

Fig. 106 shows this method of construction.

RECESSES LEFT FOR END OF JOISTS
9"×2" JOISTS
4"×3" WALL PLATE IN WALL

Fig. 106

Floor-boards.—These are usually laid direct on the top edge of the timber joists. The method of securing the boards to the joists will depend upon the type of boards being used, viz. : Hard-wood boards should be prepared for secret nailing and deal boards prepared with square, dowelled, grooved, tongued, ploughed and tongued joints to suit the requirements of any particular case.

In all instances narrow boards are better than wide ones and the boards should be cut so that the annual rings are approximately perpendicular to the surface.

Wood blocks are often used for covering solid concrete and hollow block floors and various methods are adopted for securing the blocks to each other and to the base. The top surface of the concrete floor should be screeded with cement and sand, to bring the surface to a uniform level, and when the screed is dry a coat of pitch and tar applied to the surface, and the blocks, after being dipped in the mixture, quickly rubbed into position.

CHAPTER XIII

CARPENTRY (*continued*)

ROOFS

THERE are two chief types of roofs :
  (1) Flat roofs.
  (2) Pitched roofs.

A flat roof will have only a slight inclination to the horizontal plane, or sufficient fall to allow the rainwater to flow to outlets.

The surfaces of pitched roofs will vary in inclination from an almost flat roof to one of extreme pitch.

The angle of pitch is often governed by the type of covering material, but the architectural design of a building may be the deciding factor in determining the pitch and the methods to be adopted in the construction of a roof.

Sometimes the pitch of a roof is referred to in the terms of the span, viz. a quarter-pitch which means that the rise or vertical height of the roof above the points of support is one-quarter the span.

' Clear span ' is the horizontal distance between the supports.

The frame-work should be referred to as the roof and the impervious materials which cover the roof as the roof-covering. There are several types of pitched roofs and they are named according to their outline.

A **lean-to roof** slopes in one direction only and is used for covering buildings of small span as in Fig. 107. The rafters are bird's-mouth jointed to a wall plate at the foot and to a wall plate at the top which may be carried on a brick corbelling course as shown.

The feet of the rafters usually overhang the face of the wall to form an eaves.

Details of the **lean-to** and **hipped roof** over the lavatories

78

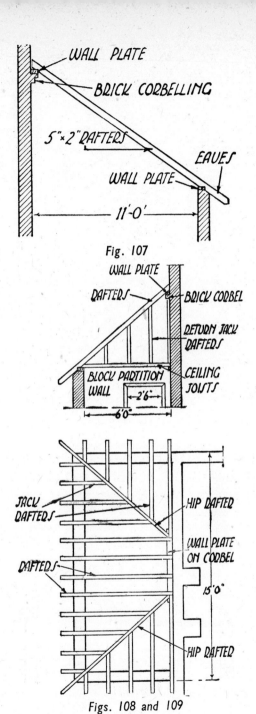

WALL PLATE

BRICK CORBELLING

5"×2" RAFTERS

EAVES

WALL PLATE

11'-0'

Fig. 107

WALL PLATE

RAFTERS

BRICK CORBEL

RETURN JACK RAFTERS

CEILING JOISTS

BLOCK PARTITION WALL

2'6"

6'0"

JACK RAFTERS

HIP RAFTER

WALL PLATE ON CORBEL

DAFTERS

15'0"

HIP RAFTER

Figs. 108 and 109

as shown in the scale drawings of the proposed Hall may be
seen in Figs. 108, 109 and 110.

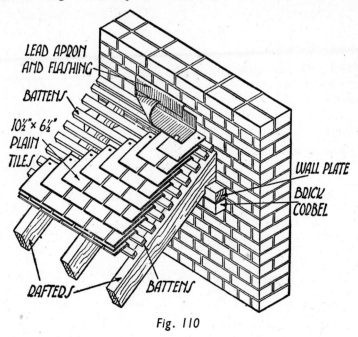

LEAD APRON
AND FLASHING

BATTENS

10½"× 6½"
PLAIN
TILES

LEAD APRON
AND FLASHING

WALL PLATE

BRICK
CORBEL

RAFTERS

BATTENS

Fig. 110

Couple roof (Fig. 111) consists of pairs of rafters, the feet
of which are bird's-mouth jointed to wall plates and the top

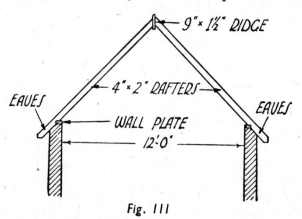

9"× 1½" RIDGE

4"× 2" RAFTERS

EAVES

EAVES

WALL PLATE

12'-0"

Fig. 111

ends are jointed against, and nailed to, a piece of timber known as a ridge board.

Couple roofs should not be used for spans exceeding 12′.

Couple Close Roof

When the span exceeds 12′, a horizontal member or tie is introduced to avoid the thrusting out of the walls and the consequent spreading of the feet of the rafters.

The best position for the ties is immediately on top of the wall plates and they may be used as ceiling joists for the support of the ceiling.

This type of roof can be used for spans up to 20′.

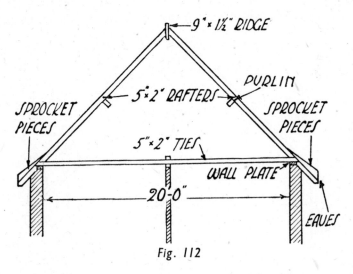

Fig. 112

To resist the tensional stresses the ties should be connected to the rafters by dovetailed and shouldered joints. Nailing for this purpose is common, but not reliable.

A section through a **couple close roof** is given in Fig. 112. For large spans, the rafters should receive intermediate support to enable them to resist any deflection which may be caused by the weight of the roof covering and the superimposed loads of snow and wind pressure.

To accomplish this, horizontal beams, termed purlins, are

placed under the rafters and about half-way up the slope of the roof.

The purlins will vary in size according to their length and method of support, and they may be placed so that their wide faces are perpendicular to the pitch of the rafters.

In certain instances the purlins will require intermediate support from diagonal struts, the feet of the struts being bird's-mouth jointed over a wall plate placed on top of a partition wall which may divide the area covered by the roof.

Collar Tie Roofs.—Roofs of this description may span up to 18'. They are constructed by connecting wood ties to the rafters one-third to one-half of the vertical height between the plates and the ridge.

This type of roof is used chiefly to obtain additional height

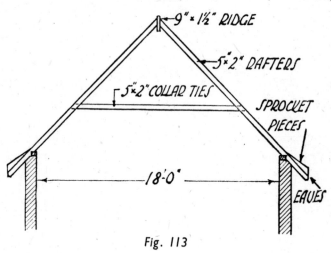

Fig. 113

for the room below, the ties acting as ceiling joists for the support of the ceiling.

When used for this purpose they should be made rigid by a form of bracing and supported from the roof at intervals across the span.

This type of roof is illustrated in the sketches showing the construction of the roof over the Billiard Hall.

Fig. 113 is a section through a collar tie roof.

HIPPED ROOFS.—When the pitched surfaces of a roof are continuous at the return end of a building, the salient angle at the intersection between the two roof slopes is termed a Hip, and the rafter which is parallel to the intersection is termed a Hip rafter.

The short rafters which are jointed to the hip rafter are termed Jack rafters. A detailed sketch is given in Fig. 114.

A **valley** in a roof surface is the re-entrant angle of two roof slopes, the rafter at the intersection is termed a valley rafter.

When the roof is not close boarded it is necessary to fix a

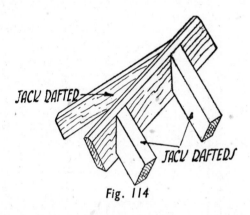

Fig. 114

board on each side of the valley to form a gutter. A sketch showing the construction of a valley is given in Fig. 149.

When a pitched roof finishes against a gable wall it is termed a gable-end and when it continues over a gable wall, the edge of the roof is called a verge.

A sketch showing the construction at the verge of a roof is given in Fig. 150.

A plan of the roof over the Billiard Hall showing the arrangement of the rafters is given in Fig. 115.

When a roof projects beyond the wall face, as in Fig. 115, the finish is usually obtained by covering the end of the roof with a wide or decorative board called a barge board.

Trimming in Roofs.—Openings in roofs for roof-lights, chimneys, etc., are trimmed in a manner similar to openings in floors, the rafters at the sides of the openings being increased

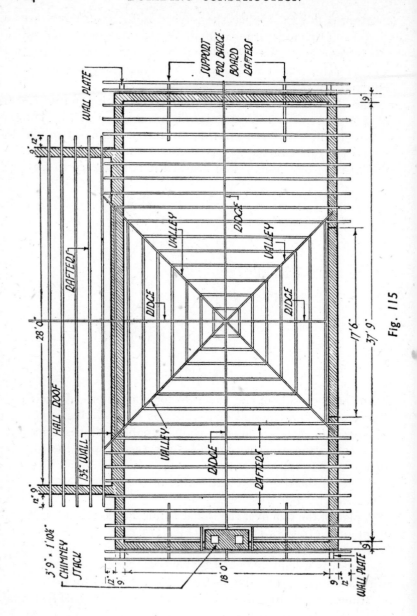

Fig. 115

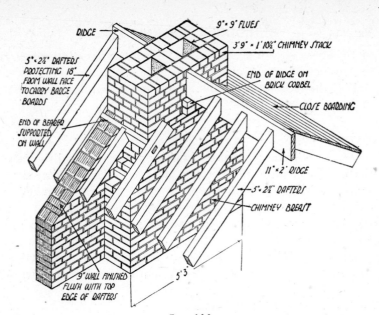

Fig. 116

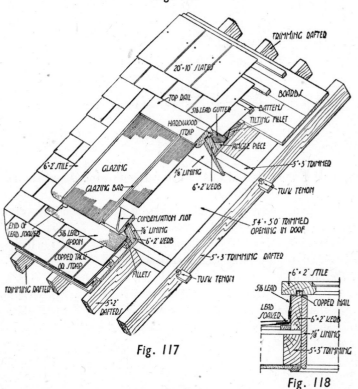

Fig. 117

Fig. 118

in thickness according to the number of rafters interrupted by the opening.

The trimming for a chimney-stack and a roof-light is shown in Figs. 116 and 117.

EAVES

When the lower ends of roof rafters project beyond the face of the wall the projection is called an eaves. There is naturally a great variety in the finish of an eaves, the rafters may be exposed or concealed and a curve may be formed in the lower portion of the roof surface by attaching sprocket pieces to the ends of the rafters.

The practical purpose of an eaves is to close the conjunction of the roof rafters with the wall construction and to provide

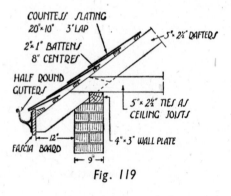

COUNTESS SLATING
20″×10″ 3′ LAP
2″×1″ BATTENS
8″ CENTRES
HALF ROUND GUTTERS
5″×2½″ RAFTERS
5″×2½″ TIES AS CEILING JOISTS
4″×3″ WALL PLATE
FASCIA BOARD
12″
9″

Fig. 119

means for the disposal of the rainwater flowing down the roof surface.

The incorporation of an efficient gutter is an important item in the design of an eaves.

The gutter should be fastened to a fascia board which is connected to the ends of the rafters.

Details of eaves are given in Figs. 119–122.

A sketch showing the construction of the eaves to the roof over the Billiard Hall, together with a detail of a dovetailed and shouldered joint between the collar tie and the rafters, is given in Fig. 123.

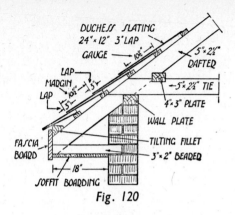

DUCHESS SLATING
24" × 12" 3" LAP
GAUGE ——— 10½"
5" × 2½"
RAFTER
LAP
MARGIN
LAP ——— 10½" 5"
—— 5" × 2½" TIE
4" × 3" PLATE
WALL PLATE
FASCIA
BOARD
TILTING FILLET
3" × 2" BEARER
18"
SOFFIT BOARDING

Fig. 120

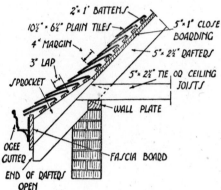

2" × 1" BATTENS
10½" × 6½" PLAIN TILES
4" MARGIN
3" LAP
SPROCKET
5" × 1" CLOSE
BOARDING
5" × 2½" RAFTERS
5" × 2½" TIE OR CEILING
JOISTS
WALL PLATE
OGEE
GUTTER
FASCIA BOARD
END OF RAFTERS
OPEN

Fig. 121

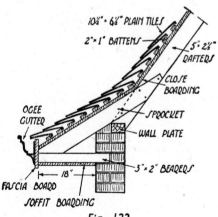

10½" × 6½" PLAIN TILES
2" × 1" BATTENS
5" × 2½"
RAFTERS
CLOSE
BOARDING
OGEE
GUTTER
SPROCKET
WALL PLATE
FASCIA BOARD
18"
3" × 2" BEARERS
SOFFIT BOARDING

Fig. 122

The fascia board is frequently used to serve as the tilting fillet, as shown in Figs. 121, 122, but it is better practice to fix the fascia board so that it has no connection with the under-eaves tiles or slates, which should rest upon the tilting fillet, as shown in Fig. 120.

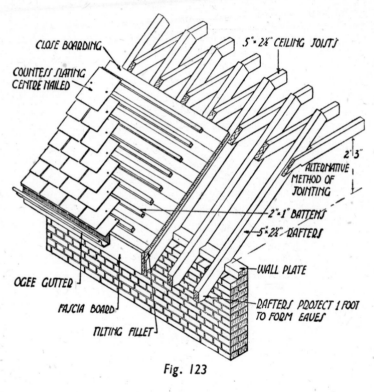

Fig. 123

CHAPTER XIV

PARTITION WALLS

Partitions are walls which divide the floor area of a building into rooms.

They may continue through two or more storeys and if they are required to carry the roof and floor loads they must be constructed in a manner suitable for this purpose and capable of supporting the loads without deflection. Until recent years, partition walls were made almost exclusively of timber framing, but in modern construction it is becoming more popular to build partition walls of fire-resisting materials.

Wood-stud partition walls are commonly known as stud partitions, their chief advantage being their lightness and they offer a good fixing for the finishings.

The wall finishings may be obtained by covering the studs with wood laths and then two or three coats of plaster, or the studs may be covered with sheets of pressed fibre board or sheets of precast plaster and then plastered.

Wood partitions may be trussed so that their weight is thrown upon the walls, but this type of partition is not used to any great extent.

A sketch showing the construction of a wood-stud partition at ground floor level, including the trimming for a doorway opening, is given in Fig. 124.

The partition framework consists of a sill-piece and head-piece, into which are housed the vertical members or studs, as shown in Fig. 125.

These should be spaced about 14″ centres and made rigid by fixing horizontal pieces of wood, termed nogging pieces, between the studs at intervals throughout the wall area.

The upright members at the sides of openings should be of larger section than the ordinary studs, and the head across

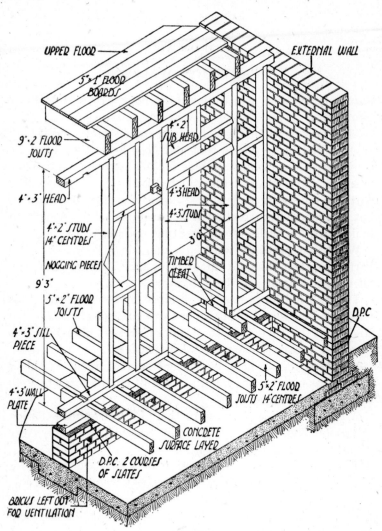

UPPER FLOOR

EXTERNAL WALL

5"×1" FLOOR
BOARDS

9"×2" FLOOR
JOISTS

4"×2"
JUB HEAD

4"×3" HEAD

4"×3" HEAD
4"×3" STUDS

4"×2" STUDS
14" CENTRES

3' 0"

NOGGING PIECES

TIMBER
CLEAT

9' 3"

5"×2" FLOOR
JOISTS

D.P.C

4"×3" SILL
PIECE

5"×2" FLOOR
JOISTS 14" CENTRES

4"×3" WALL
PLATE

CONCRETE
SURFACE LAYER

D.P.C. 2 COURSES
OF SLATES

BRICKS LEFT OUT
FOR VENTILATION

Fig. 124

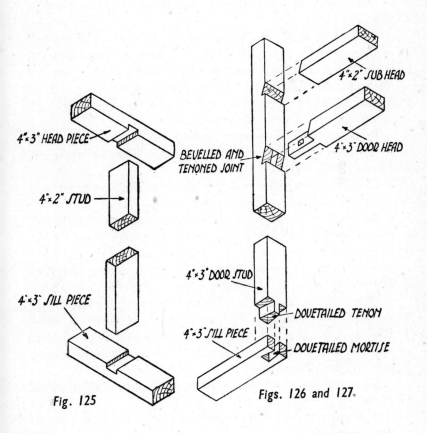

4"×3" HEAD PIECE

4"×2" STUD

4"×3" SILL PIECE

BEVELLED AND TENONED JOINT

4"×2" SUB HEAD

4"×3" DOOR HEAD

4"×3" DOOR STUD

DOVETAILED TENON

4"×3" SILL PIECE

DOVETAILED MORTISE

Fig. 125

Figs. 126 and 127.

the opening joined to the door studs by means of a bevelled and tenoned joint, as shown in Fig. 126.

To prevent the head sagging, should a load be concentrated on the floor immediately above the partition, a sub-head may be introduced just above the headpiece, as shown in the sketch.

A detail of the joint at the foot of the door stud is given in Fig. 127.

Steel Mesh Partition Walls.—Wood studs may be covered with some form of expanded metal instead of wood laths, or metal studs may be used instead of wood and then covered with expanded metal and finished with plaster.

The layers of plaster on each side of the framework will assist the wall to become rigid.

Brick partition walls may be built as load-carrying walls, and if crowned with a wall plate they may assist in supporting the loads of the floors and roof.

Details showing the construction of a brick partition wall are given in Figs. 128 and 129.

The wall is shown built up from the concrete foundations and a steel flat is introduced to act as a wall plate for the support of the ends of the ground floor joists.

A reinforced concrete lintol is shown spanning the door opening to assist in carrying the loads from the floor above.

Slab Partition Walls.—Special precast breeze or plaster slabs are used sometimes for the construction of partition walls. The slabs have keyed vertical and horizontal joint surfaces and the face surfaces are roughened and grooved to form a key for the plaster finish.

Fig. 132 illustrates the construction of a slab partition wall.

Burnt Clay Block Partition Walls.—Hollow terra-cotta blocks of varying dimensions are in general use for the construction of partition walls. The blocks are keyed and grooved on the faces and the cavities are open at the ends.

This type of partition wall may be built up from the concrete surface layer, but is unsuitable when commencing from a timber upper floor.

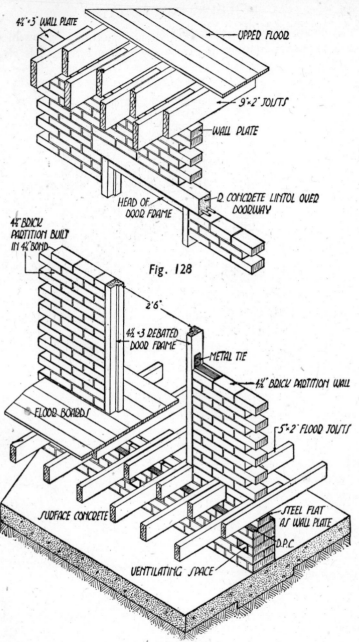

4½"×3" WALL PLATE

UPPER FLOOR

9"×2" JOISTS

WALL PLATE

HEAD OF DOOR FRAME

R. CONCRETE LINTOL OVER DOORWAY

Fig. 128

4½" BRICK PARTITION BUILT IN 4½" BOND

2'6"

4½"×3" REBATED DOOR FRAME

METAL TIE

4½" BRICK PARTITION WALL

FLOOR BOARDS

5"×2" FLOOR JOISTS

SURFACE CONCRETE

STEEL FLAT AS WALL PLATE

D.P.C.

VENTILATING SPACE

Fig. 129

A constructional sketch showing a portion of a hollow block partition wall commencing from a solid concrete floor is given in Fig. 130.

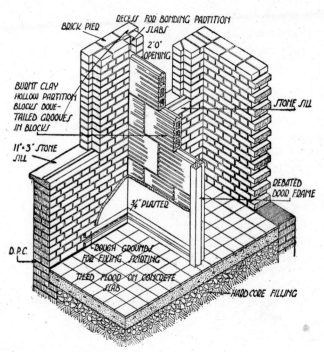

Fig. 130

CHAPTER XV

JOINERY

JOINERY is distinguished from carpentry by the character of the work and by the fact that it comprises the fittings and finishings to buildings. Doors, door-frames, window-frames and sashes, linings, panelling, stairs, etc., are included in the term finishings.

Doors

Doors may be divided into four classes :
(1) Battened and ledged doors.
(2) Framed and braced doors.
(3) Framed and panelled doors.
(4) Flush doors.

The type and most suitable construction of a door is governed by the position in which it is to be used and the character of the surrounding work.

Battened and ledged doors are constructed of ploughed and tongued boards from $\frac{5}{8}''$ to $1''$ thick, which are nailed to three horizontal boards, known as ledges.

An improvement in this type of door is obtained by securing inclined bracing pieces between the ledges as shown in Fig. 131, and arranged so as to support the free side of the door.

Framed and braced doors consist of two stiles and top rail the full thickness of the door, and the middle or lock rail and the bottom rail and braces less than the full thickness of the stiles by the thickness of the boards. This arrangement of the timbers will produce a flush face on the exterior surface of the door (Fig. 134).

The battens should be tongued to the stiles and top rail and the rails tenoned into the stiles.

Framed panelled doors consist of a frame filled in with wood or glass panels.

The outside upright members are termed stiles, and the top and bottom cross-pieces the rails.

In a three or four-panelled door the centre cross-piece is termed the lock rail and the centre upright member the munting.

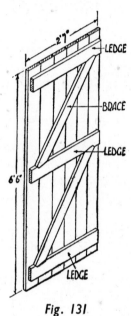

Fig. 131

The rails are tenoned into the outside stiles and the munting is tenoned into the lock rail and the top or bottom rail.

The panels are held in grooves cut in the inner edges of the frame or by mouldings planted on to the frame. To allow for any shrinkage or swelling, the panels should not be fixed rigid but allowed to move freely in the grooves, or between the mouldings.

A great variety in the design of doors can be obtained by changing the number of panels and the position of the muntings and lock rails.

A constructional sketch of a three-panelled door, which

forms part of the internal finishings to one of the compartments shown on the scale drawings, is given in Fig. 132.

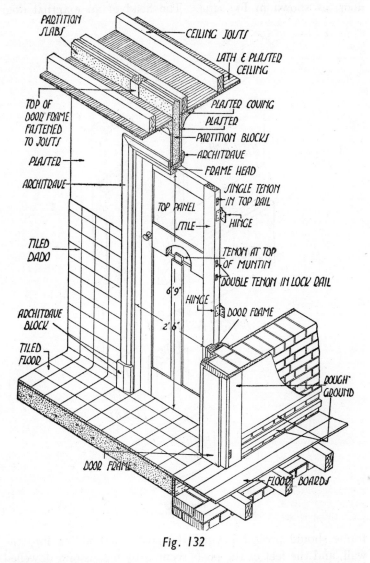

PARTITION SLABS

CEILING JOISTS

LATH & PLASTER CEILING

TOP OF DOOR FRAME FASTENED TO JOISTS

PLASTER COVING

PLASTER

PARTITION BLOCKS

ARCHITRAVE

PLASTER

FRAME HEAD

ARCHITRAVE

SINGLE TENON IN TOP RAIL

TOP PANEL

STILE

HINGE

TILED DADO

TENON AT TOP OF MUNTIN

DOUBLE TENON IN LOCK RAIL

6'9"

HINGE

DOOR FRAME

ARCHITRAVE BLOCK

2'6"

TILED FLOOR

ROUGH GROUND

DOOR FRAME

FLOOR BOARDS

Fig. 132

Details of the joints between the stiles and rails are given in Fig. 133.

Door frames are usually made from $4'' \times 3''$ timber, and consist of posts and head, each member being rebated for the door, as shown in Fig. 134. The head of an external door

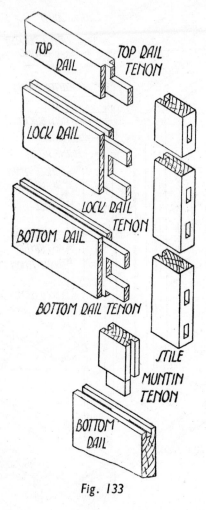

Fig. 133

frame should project beyond the posts for building into the wall, and the feet of the posts secured by means of a dowelled joint between the posts and the threshold, the posts being tenoned into the head and wedged or pinned (Fig. 134).

In Fig. 132 the door jambs continue beyond the head and are fastened to the ceiling joists.

Door Linings.—The framing around internal door openings are called linings. They may be cased or built-up to suit the width of the door jamb which will vary with the type and thickness of the wall.

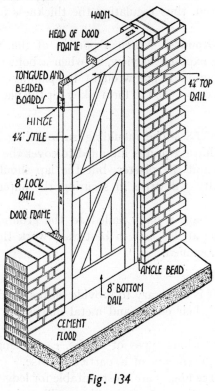

HODM

HEAD OF DOOD
FDAME

TONGUED AND
BEADED
BOARDS

4¼" TOP
DAIL

HINGE

4¼" STILE

8" LOCK
DAIL

DOOD FDAME

ANGLE BEAD

8" BOTTOM
DAIL

CEMENT
FLOOD

Fig. 134

Framed linings are generally used for doorway openings in brick walls over 9″ thick, and the construction of the linings will vary according to the finish required. They may be framed and panelled, or solid and rebated to form the door stop. In any case, the panel or rebate should be continuous across the head.

The linings for a 9″ wall are shown in Fig. 132.

Grounds are strips of wood fixed to the brickwork by means of wood plugs or fixing bricks and form the base upon which joinery can be screwed or nailed.

Rough grounds are left from the saw and should be entirely covered by the joinery, and when they are intended to be adjoined by plaster-work they should be edge-bevelled to form a key for the plaster. They are used by the plasterer as a guide or screed, thus regulating the thickness of the plaster-work.

Wrought Grounds.—When a portion of the grounds is intended to be exposed to view, or when a bolder architrave is desired, the grounds are wrought by planing and the outer edge splayed or bevelled to form a key for the plaster as already described.

ARCHITRAVES.—The moulding surrounding a doorway is called an architrave and is intended to cover the joint between the grounds and the plaster, but the lap should not exceed $\frac{1}{2}''$ or difficulty will arise in securing the outer edge of the architrave.

Architraves are usually nailed to the grounds and mitre-jointed at the angles, but in best-class work they are mitre-jointed and tenoned.

DOOR FURNITURE

Hinges.—It is necessary to provide means for doors to swing about one of their edges, and metal hinges are used for this purpose.

There are various types of hinges, each being designed to meet the requirements of a particular case.

Garnet or Tee hinges are most suitable for ledged or battened doors, because the arm of the hinge will assist in supporting the overhanging portion of the door.

Butt hinges are in common use for pivoting frame doors. For ordinary work they are made of malleable iron or steel, but for better-class work they are made of brass, gunmetal and chromium-plated steel.

Latches of various forms are used for securing battened doors, but their use is only a means for securing a door in position and not to act as a locking device.

The term latch is often given to a lock which combines the function of a latch with a security of a lock, such as a night latch.

Locks provide a means for securing and locking a door, the commonest types are the ' rim ' lock and the ' mortise ' lock.

The rim lock is fastened on the inside face of the door, and the mortise lock is fitted in a mortise, cut in the edge of the door.

Door furniture also includes handles, key plates, Picking plates and other accessories.

CHAPTER XVI

JOINERY (*continued*)

WINDOW FRAMES AND SASHES

WINDOWS may be divided into classes according to the manner of hanging the sashes, viz. :

(1) Casement.
(2) Double hung.
(3) Pivotted.
(4) Sliding.

SOLID FRAMES AND CASEMENT SASHES

A solid window-frame consists of posts, sill and head with occasionally an intermediate horizontal member termed a transome or a vertical member termed a mullion.

The posts and head are rebated for the sashes and moulded if desired.

Sills are generally made of oak or teak, the upper surface of the sill being rebated and weathered to assist in keeping the rainwater from penetrating to the interior of the window-frame.

When a wood sill surmounts a stone sill, a groove should be made in the lower surface of the wood sill, the position of the groove corresponding with a groove cut in the top surface of the stone sill.

A metal bar is inserted in the groove, half of the bar being in the wood sill and half in the stone sill and the wood sill bedded in red lead to ensure a watertight joint.

When a wood sill surmounts a brick or tile sill a large groove may be cut in the under-surface of the wood sill and fixed on a cement mortar bed which should fill the cavity in the under-side of the wood sill. If properly carried out, this procedure will ensure a watertight joint between the two sills.

Transomes are shaped in section similar to the sill but the underside of the transome is rebated for the lower sashes.

A transome should be wider than the frame, to enable a groove to be cut in the under-surface to form a drip.

Mullions are shaped in section similar to double posts.

Sashes are the glazed frames which are fitted into the window-frames. Sashes are often divided into smaller areas by means of sash bars.

Sashes may be :

(1) Rigidly fixed to the frame.
(2) Hinged at the sides to open inwards or outwards.
(3) Hinged at the top or bottom.
(4) Arranged to slide in grooves horizontally.
(5) Arranged to slide in grooves vertically.
(6) Pivotted to rotate about a vertical axis.
(7) Pivotted to rotate about a horizontal axis.

Sashes opening outwards are more easily made watertight than those opening inwards.

Inaccessibility for cleaning is one disadvantage, but this objection may be eliminated by fitting a special type of hinge which will rotate the sash clear of the frame, thus bringing the external glazing surface into an accessible position.

A constructional sketch of a casement window-frame, including transome, mullion and sashes, is given in Fig. 135.

The lower sashes are shown side-hinged to open outwards and the upper sashes top-hinged to open outwards. A section through the window opening is given in Fig. 136.

When sashes open inwards, provision must be made for the deflection of the rainwater.

This may be done by fixing a weather board to the lower external portion of the sash or by fixing a metal strip to the sill.

Details through the hard-wood sill and the transome are given in Figs. 137 and 138.

CASED OR BOXED WINDOW-FRAMES

The posts and head of cased window-frames are built up of several members so as to form vertical casings, in which are

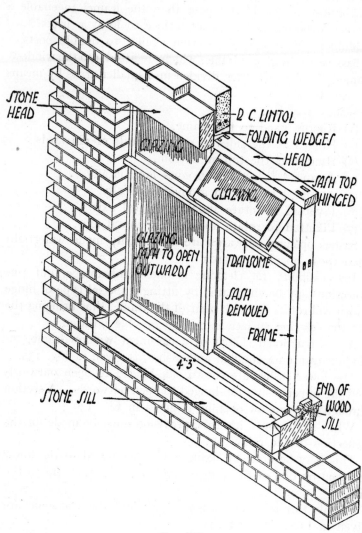

STONE HEAD

R. C. LINTOL

FOLDING WEDGES

HEAD

GLAZING

SASH TOP HINGED

GLAZING

GLAZING SASH TO OPEN OUTWARDS

TRANSOME

SASH REMOVED

FRAME

4'3"

STONE SILL

END OF WOOD SILL

Fig. 135

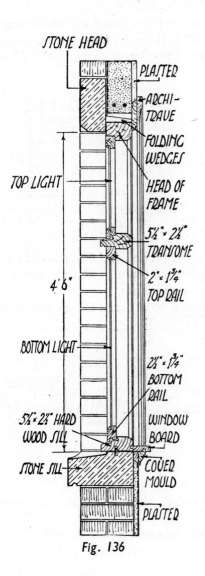

STONE HEAD

PLASTER

ARCHI-
TRAVE

FOLDING
WEDGES

HEAD OF
FRAME

TOP LIGHT

$5\frac{1}{2}" \times 2\frac{1}{2}"$
TRANSOME

$2" \times 1\frac{3}{4}"$
TOP RAIL

4' 6"

BOTTOM LIGHT

$2\frac{1}{2}" \times 1\frac{3}{4}"$
BOTTOM
RAIL

$5\frac{1}{2}" \times 2\frac{1}{2}"$ HARD
WOOD SILL

WINDOW
BOARD

STONE SILL

COVER
MOULD

PLASTER

Fig. 136

housed the balancing weights which assist in the easy sliding movement of the sashes.

In frames of this kind there are usually two sashes, each sliding vertically in its own pair of grooves, which are formed in the posts and separated by a parting-bead or fillet.

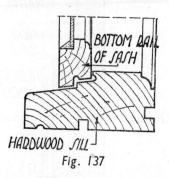

Fig. 137

Each sash is suspended by being attached to suspended weights by means of cords or chains, which are contained in the casings in the posts.

The construction of a boxed frame and sliding sashes, to-

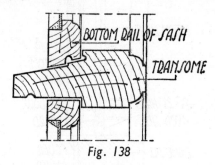

Fig. 138

gether with the sizes of the parts and important details, can be seen in Fig. 139.

The sill should be made of oak or teak, and does not differ very considerably in section from that under a solid window-frame.

Detail sections through the sill, jamb and head of the window-frame and sashes are given in Figs. 140, 141 and 142.

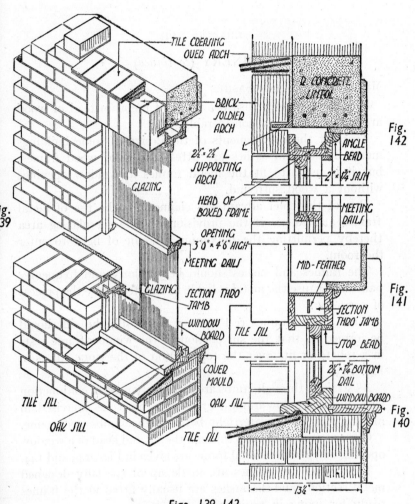

TILE CREASING OVER ARCH

BRICK SOLDIER ARCH

2½"×2½" L SUPPORTING ARCH

HEAD OF BOXED FRAME

OPENING 3'0"×4'6" HIGH

MEETING RAILS

GLAZING

SECTION THRO' JAMB

WINDOW BOARD

GLAZING

TILE SILL

OAK SILL

COVER MOULD

OAK SILL

TILE SILL

Fig. 139

R. CONCRETE LINTOL

ANGLE BEAD

2"×1¾" SASH

MEETING RAILS

Fig. 142

MID-FEATHER

SECTION THRO' JAMB

STOP BEAD

TILE SILL

Fig. 141

2½"×1¾" BOTTOM RAIL

WINDOW BOARD

Fig. 140

13½"

Figs. 139-142

CHAPTER XVII

JOINERY (*continued*)

METAL FRAMES AND SASHES

Window-frames and sashes made of metal instead of wood are being used very considerably.

To meet the requirements of the design of some buildings metal frames and sashes are fitted into solid wood frames, but it is usual to fit the metal frames in window openings without a wood surround.

One of the chief advantages claimed for the use of metal frames and sashes is the provision of a larger glazing area thereby permitting the maximum amount of light to enter the room.

The frames and sashes should be regularly and frequently painted because the metal is liable to be affected by the process of corrosion.

When metal frames rest upon a stone sill, the sill should be formed so that the sill portion of the window-frame rests in a rebate or fits over the top portion of the stone sill as in Fig. 143.

As straight-through jambs are commonly used in conjunction with metal window-frames, great care must be exercised in making the joints watertight between the jambs and frame.

Constructional sketches through the sill and head of a window opening fitted with a metal frame are given in Figs. 143 and 144.

The frames and sashes are made up of specially designed metal sections, and the sashes are usually fitted in the frames ready for fixing in position on the site.

Internal finishings to windows consist chiefly of a window board which acts as an inside sill and projects beyond the face of the internal plaster-work to form a seating for the architrave moulding. The underside of the window board should be

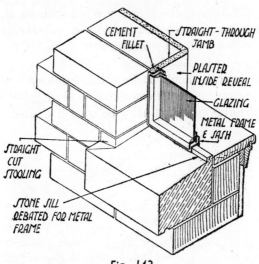

Fig. 143

finished with a thickness mould, tongued into the window
board and fastened to a splayed rough ground. The internal
reveals to window openings are usually finished with plaster

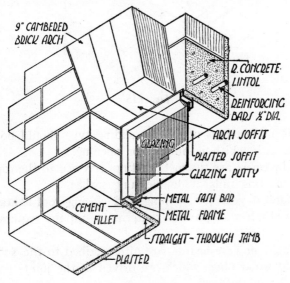

Fig. 144

and the joint against the frame covered with an angle bead, but wood linings are desired sometimes to cover the inside reveal, in which case the construction is similar to that described for internal door linings.

Window fittings should include the following :

Hinges.—Butt hinges are commonly used for casement sashes but special forms of hinges may be used if desired.

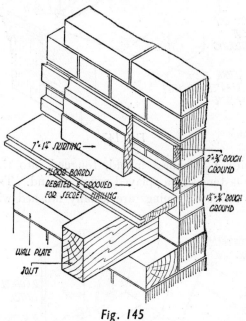

Fig. 145

Casement fasteners of the pin sliding type should be fitted to each sash which is hinged for opening.

Sash fasteners are the metal fittings screwed to the top edge of the meeting rails of double-hung sashes.

Mechanical gear for opening and closing roof-lights, etc., may be obtained in various patterns to suit the requirements of any particular case.

Skirtings, or base-boards, are often scribed to the floor and nailed to wood plugs which are driven in the joints between the bricks in the wall.

Shrinkage of the timber often results in a space being formed between the bottom edge of the skirting and the floor-boards, but this defect may be overcome by fastening an angle bead to the floor-boards. A better method is to tongue the bottom edge of the skirting into a groove cut in the floor-boards.

Skirtings should be fixed to grounds fastened to the wall in a horizontal or vertical position.

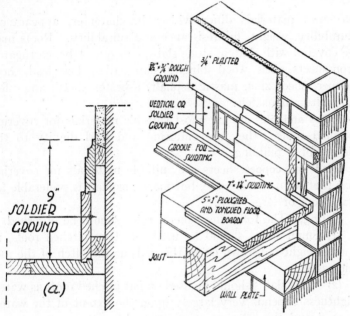

Fig. 146

When fixed horizontally, the top edge of the upper grounds should be bevelled to form a key for the plaster-work and the top edge of the skirting-board should just cover the joint.

When the grounds are fixed vertically, they are termed soldier grounds and are placed about 3' apart, and their function is to assist in securing or fixing a built-up skirting, as shown in Fig. 146 (a). To improve the method of fixing and avoid joint plugging, fixing bricks may be built in the wall in suitable positions. Breeze bricks are very suitable for this purpose.

Details of skirtings are given in Figs. 145 and 146.

CHAPTER XVIII

ROOF COVERINGS

ROOFING materials differ widely in character, appearance, durability, weight, fire-resistance and suitability. Roofs may be covered with thatch, stone slabs, concrete slabs, corrugated iron sheets, glass, wood shingles, slates, tiles, sheet lead, sheet copper, sheet zinc, mastic asphalt, asbestos sheets and tiles, and bituminous felt.

Slates and tiles are the most suitable materials for covering pitched roofs; they are enduring and lend dignity to the design of a building.

Lead and copper sheets are suitable materials for covering flat roofs of moderate size, but mastic asphalt is preferable for flat roofs of large area.

Slating.—The following general rules should be observed.

(1) Small slates should be used for steep pitched roofs, as more weight is thrown on to the nails as the pitch of the roof increases.

(2) Wide slates should be used on flat pitched roofs as water-tightness depends very largely upon the extent of the water-spread and the relation of width to length.

If the pitch of the roof is less than 30°, slates 12″ wide are suitable, as they will minimise the number of vertical joints and increase the cover between the joints and the nail-holes in the course of slates immediately below.

The names and sizes of slates in most general use are :

Duchess 24″ long by 12″ wide.
Countess 20″ ,, ,, 10″ ,,
Ladies 16″ ,, ,, 8″ ,,

(3) **Lap** is the distance by which each slate overlaps the next but one below it.

The roof pitch is the primary factor in determining the

amount of lap, but 3″ may be taken as the standard measurement.

The margin is the part of each slate which is exposed to view on a roof surface.

The gauge is the distance from centre to centre of the battens and is the same distance as the margin. The gauge for centre-nailed slates may be determined by deducting the lap from the length of the slate and dividing the remainder by 2.

The bed is the under-surface of a slate when laid on the roof surface.

The head is the top edge of a slate when laid on a roof surface.

The following is the British Standard specification with reference to slates :

Size in Inches.	Gauge 3-in. Lap Centre-nailed.	No. of Squares covered by 1200.	No. of Slates per 100 Sq. Ft.	Weight of Slates, Nails and Battens (lb. per Sq. Ft.)
24 × 12 . .	10½″	10	125	5¾
20 × 10 . .	8½″	7	171	5½
16 × 8 . .	6½″	4	300	5½

Slates may be nailed at the head or in the centre. Centre-nailing is probably the best and most common method adopted.

Head-nailed slates are liable to displacement by winds, but they provide a better cover for the nails.

Slates may be fixed to battens nailed direct to the roof rafters, or the roof may be close-boarded and battened.

Roofing felt may be used in preference to or in conjunction with boarding.

Slating Nails.—Copper or composition nails should be used in preference to iron nails.

Composition nails are made from an alloy of copper and zinc.

To use inferior quality nails is false economy as much expense may be occasioned by the replacement of slates. Two nails should be used for each slate.

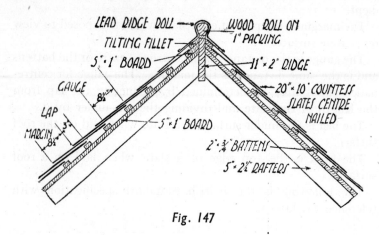

LEAD RIDGE ROLL
TILTING FILLET
5"×1" BOARD
GAUGE 8½"
LAP 3"
MARGIN 8½"
5"×1" BOARD
WOOD ROLL ON 1" PACKING
11"×2" RIDGE
20"×10" COUNTESS SLATES CENTRE NAILED
2"×¾" BATTENS
5"×2½" RAFTERS

Fig. 147

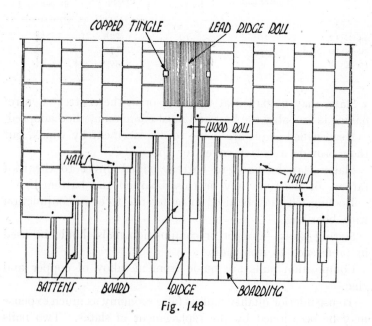

COPPED TINGLE   LEAD RIDGE ROLL
WOOD ROLL
NAILS
NAILS
BATTENS   BOARD   RIDGE   BOARDING

Fig. 148

Slating at Eaves.—A double course of slates is placed at an eaves so that the margin of the first course will have two thicknesses of slates.

The length of the under slates at an eaves equals the margin plus the lap, and when the slates are head-nailed an extra inch in length should be allowed.

In order that the slates may rest properly on the roof surface a tilting fillet is placed at the lower edge of a roof to tilt up the lower courses.

Details showing slating at eaves are given in Figs. 119, 120 and 123.

Slating at Ridges.—A double course of slates may be placed at the ridge of the roof, but water-tightness can be maintained by using a thicker batten, or preferably a double batten, which will allow the topmost course of slates to be nailed and covering the ridge with sheet lead to form the lap necessary.

The ridge may be covered with slate slabs specially worked in the form of ridge tiles or with burnt clay ridge tiles.

Details through a slated ridge are given in Figs. 147 and 148.

SLATING AT VALLEYS AND HIPS

Slates are cut obliquely to fit the angles or intersections of roof surfaces.

A valley may be covered with sheet lead, dressed in the form of a gutter, to carry off the rainwater, the slates at the side of the valley gutter being of double width and cut with one edge parallel with the gutter, as shown in Fig. 149, or the slates may be close-mitred and laid in conjunction with lead soakers.

Slates at hips may be close-mitred and lead soakers introduced, but it is preferable to cover the intersection of the roof surfaces with sheet lead similar to the ridge. Ridge tiles may be used if desired and bedded solid on a mortar bed.

Slating over Verges.—When slating projects over a wall an additional course of slates should be laid on the wall beneath the battens and the space filled with cement mortar, as shown in Fig. 150.

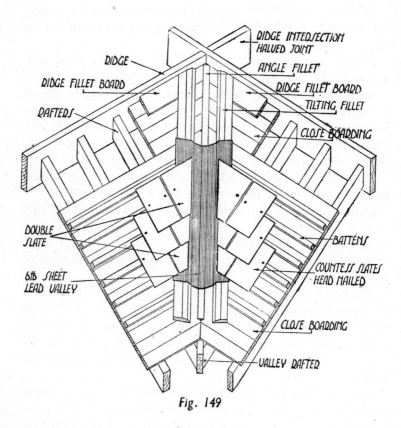

RIDGE INTERSECTION HALVED JOINT

ANGLE FILLET

RIDGE

RIDGE FILLET BOARD

RIDGE FILLET BOARD

TILTING FILLET

RAFTERS

CLOSE BOARDING

DOUBLE SLATE

BATTENS

6lb SHEET LEAD VALLEY

COUNTESS SLATES HEAD NAILED

CLOSE BOARDING

VALLEY RAFTER

Fig. 149

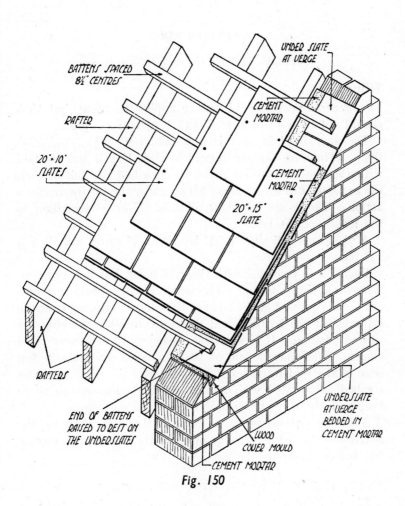

Fig. 150

BATTENS SPACED 8½" CENTRES

RAFTER

20"×10" SLATES

RAFTERS

END OF BATTENS RAISED TO REST ON THE UNDERSLATES

CEMENT MORTAR

CEMENT MORTAR

20"×15" SLATE

UNDER SLATE AT VERGE

WOOD COVER MOULD

CEMENT MORTAR

UNDERSLATE AT VERGE BEDDED IN CEMENT MORTAR

CHAPTER XIX

ROOF COVERINGS (*continued*)

Tiling

THE general principles of slating applies to tiling, but tiles should not be used on a roof with less than 45° pitch.

The size of plain tiles is approximately $10\frac{1}{2}'' \times 6\frac{1}{2}'' \times \frac{1}{2}''$ thick. They are slightly curved in their length and are laid with the concave surface down to close-bed the tail of each tile to prevent moisture being drawn under the tile by capillary action. The gauge for plain tiling is $3\frac{1}{2}''$ or $4''$ according to the length of the lap.

A $3\frac{1}{2}''$ gauge will allow a $3\frac{1}{2}''$ lap and a $4''$ gauge will allow a $2\frac{1}{2}''$ lap.

Each tile is provided with two nail-holes, but it is not considered necessary to nail each course, because projecting nibs are usually formed at the head of the tiles for clipping over the top edge of the battens, and these will assist in keeping the tiles in position. It is advisable, however, to nail every third course. Tiles may be laid on battens nailed direct to the top edge of the roof rafters, but in such cases the tiles should be torched or pointed with mortar on the underside so as to keep out the wind or driving rain.

A better method is to close-board the roof, then fix the battens to the required gauge or cover the rafters with roofing felt before fixing the battens.

TILING AT EAVES, RIDGE, HIPS, AND VALLEYS

The eaves of a roof covered with plain tiles is treated in a manner similar to a slated eaves.

A double course of tiles is placed at the commencement of the eaves and tilted on a tilting fillet, but it is advisable to close the underside of the eaves with soffit boarding.

Details of tiled eaves are given in Figs. 121 and 122. Details of the tiling at the ridge of a roof are given in Figs. 151 and 152.

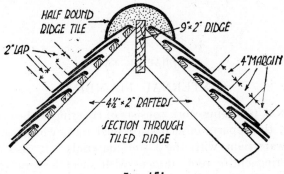

Fig. 151

Many special forms of ridge tiles are manufactured, the simplest being half-round tiles.

They should be of sufficient width to form the required lap

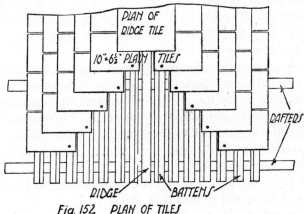

Fig. 152   PLAN OF TILES
AT RIDGE OF ROOF

with the tiles in the course below the top course and bedded solid in cement mortar.

Special hip tiles are manufactured and can be obtained to suit the angle and pitch of the roof.

CHAPTER XX

EXTERNAL PLUMBING

EXTERNAL plumbing-work consists of covering with sheet lead, or zinc, those parts on slated or tiled roofs which cannot be made watertight with the latter materials. It also consists of covering entire roof surfaces with sheet lead or zinc and includes the provision of means for the effective discharge and conveyance of the rainwater from roof surfaces.

The covering of the exposed top surfaces of projecting courses, such as stone cornices, etc., with sheet lead may be considered as part of external plumbing work. Sheet lead is the best metal for covering flats, dormers, and forming gutters, flashings, etc., because of its lasting properties and ease with which it may be ' bossed ' or worked to almost any shape, thus avoiding the use of solder.

In common with other metals, lead expands and contracts with alternating temperatures, therefore it is important that provision be made for its free movement by regulating the size of the sheets and careful arrangement of the joints, otherwise fractures and buckling will result. Single sheets should not exceed 8' × 3' 6", nailing resorted to as little as possible and soldering avoided.

The joints between the sheets of lead should be formed by means of laps, welts, rolls and drips.

Wood rolls are required for covering the joints at the ridge of a pitched roof or for forming the joints on lead flats and at the highest point of a lead gutter when the water flows from right to left.

They should be fixed to the roof timbering and under-cut so that the lead when dressed is held securely in position.

Sheet lead should be laid on close-boarding specially pre-

pared with smooth surfaces, and the boards laid with the grain
in the direction of the flow of the water.

Soakers.—When slated or tiled roofs abutt against walls,
chimney-stacks, ventilation turrets, roof-lights, dormer

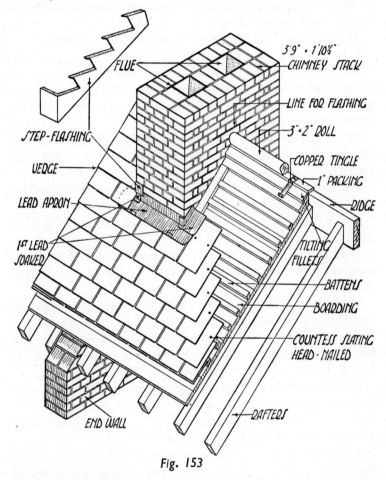

Fig. 153

windows, etc., the joints may be rendered watertight by the
inclusion of small pieces of lead termed soakers, which are
bent to a right angle, one part being placed against the vertical
surface and the remaining portion under the tail of each slate
or tile.

The length of the soakers equals the gauge plus the lap of each course of slates or tiles and an extra inch should be allowed for the lead to be clipped over the top edge of the slate or tile or for nailing just above the top edge.

The number of soakers can be deduced from the number of courses of slates or tiles.

Figs. 118 and 153 illustrate the use of lead soakers.

COVER FLASHINGS.—The vertical portion of the soakers which rest against a vertical surface should be capped or covered with strips or pieces of lead which are turned into a groove formed in the walling material or in the bed-joints of the brickwork.

When pitched roof-surfaces abutt brickwork, the flashing is stepped to accommodate the heights of the horizontal brick courses.

Flashings are secured in the wall by means of wedges and the joints pointed with mastic or cement mortar.

Cover flashings against a chimney-stack and gable wall are illustrated in Figs. 153 and 157.

Lead gutters may be formed between the foot of a pitched roof and a parapet wall or between two pitched roofs. They should have a fall of about 1½" in 10' towards an outlet.

Where the design of a building will permit, it is advisable to arrange the boarding so that the surface of the gutter falls in two directions from the centre, thus economising in lead, because the highest point of a gutter at the foot of a pitched roof is necessarily its widest point.

Such gutters are termed tapering gutters and when they are formed at the foot of a pitched roof and behind a parapet wall they are termed parapet gutters, as shown in Fig. 154. The length of the pieces of lead in gutters should not exceed 8' and they should be joined by forming a drip at least 2" in depth, as in Fig. 155, the two sheets of lead being lapped and the lead at the highest point dressed over a wood roll, as shown in Fig. 156.

The lead sheets should be dressed over the tilting fillet fixed to the lower part of the roof surface and then covered with the lower courses of slates or tiles, the other edge being

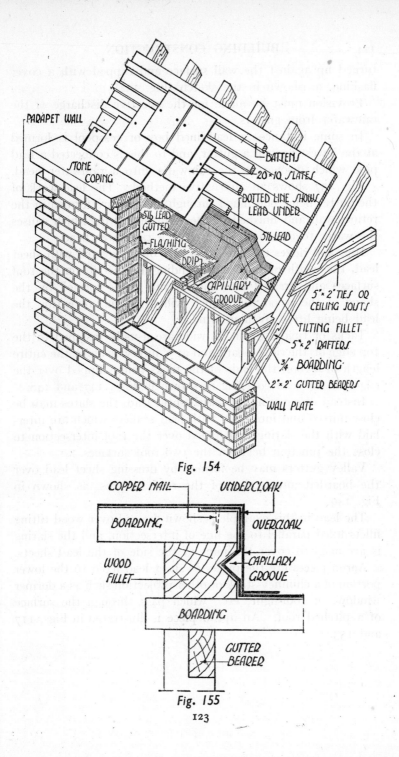

PARAPET WALL

STONE
COPING

BATTENS

20×10 SLATES

DOTTED LINE SHOWS
LEAD UNDER

5lb LEAD
GUTTER

FLASHING

5lb LEAD

DRIP

CAPILLARY
GROOVE

5"×2" TIES OR
CEILING JOISTS

TILTING FILLET

5"×2" RAFTERS

¾" BOARDING

2"×2" GUTTER BEARERS

WALL PLATE

Fig. 154

COPPER NAIL

UNDERCLOAK

BOARDING

OVERCLOAK

WOOD
FILLET

CAPILLARY
GROOVE

BOARDING

GUTTER
BEARER

Fig. 155

123

turned up against the wall surface and capped with a cover flashing, as shown in the sketch (Fig. 154).

Provision must be made for the effective discharge of the rainwater from gutters.

In some instances a lead-lined box or cesspool is formed at the lowest part of a gutter, and to this is connected a lead pipe which discharges the rainwater into a rainwater head.

Fig. 157 shows an alternative method : The lead-work of the gutter being continued through an aperture formed in the return wall and finished in the form of a drip, which causes the water to discharge direct into a rainwater head.

Hips and ridges to slated roofs are often covered with sheet lead, the width of the lead extending at least 6″ on the roof surfaces and dressed into the internal angle formed by the shape of the wood roll, which will assist in preventing the lead being lifted by high winds.

Tacks or tingles about 2″ wide are usually fastened to the top edge of the ridge board and at 3′ intervals along the entire length of a roof, the ends of the tacks being clipped over the edges of the lead covering as shown in Figs. 147 and 148.

Instead of covering hips with sheet lead, the slates may be close-mitred and interlined with lead soakers which are inter-laid with the slating and folded over the roof intersection to close the junction between the two roof surfaces.

Valley gutters may be formed by dressing sheet lead over the boarded intersection of the roof surfaces, as shown in Fig. 149.

The lead in this example is shown dressed over wood tilting fillets fixed parallel to the line of intersection, and the slating is arranged to cover the joint at the side of the lead sheets.

Apron pieces are the pieces of sheet lead fixed to the lower portion of a chimney-stack or other projection such as a dormer window, or roof-light, etc., which pass through the surface of a pitched roof. An apron piece is illustrated in Figs. 117 and 153.

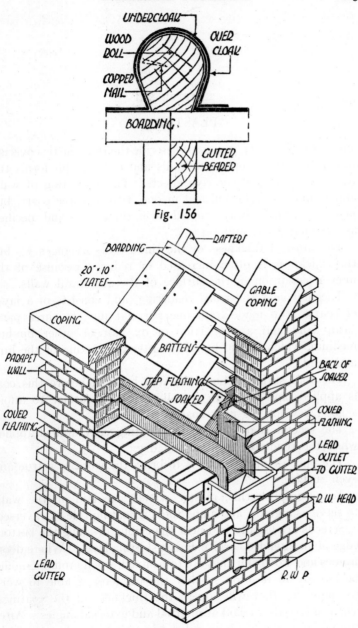

Fig. 156

Fig. 156 labels: UNDERCLOAK, WOOD ROLL, OVER CLOAK, COPPER NAIL, BOARDING, GUTTER BEARER

Fig. 157 labels: RAFTERS, BOARDING, 20" × 10" SLATES, GABLE COPING, COPING, PARAPET WALL, BATTENS, STEP FLASHING, SOAKER, BACK OF SOAKER, COVER FLASHING, COVER FLASHING, LEAD OUTLET TO GUTTER, R.W. HEAD, LEAD GUTTER, R.W.P.

Fig. 157.

CHAPTER XXI

PLASTERING

The term plastering is used to describe the thin plastic covering which is usually applied to walls and ceiling, and forms the base for internal decorative effects. The plastering of walls and ceilings may be finished in one, two or three coats, but in best work it is always carried out in three coats and specified as 'render, float, and set.'

The finished thickness of the three coats averages $\frac{3}{4}''$, but this thickness is often increased or reduced because of the uneven condition of the surface of the structural walls.

The first coat is termed rendering, and consists of a layer of coarse stuff made from one part fat lime to three parts clean sand and a proportion of ox hair or other binding medium, which should be added after the mixing of the lime and sand.

The wall surfaces should be well brushed before this coat is applied, and left with a well-roughened surface to afford a good key for the next coat.

The second coat is termed a floating coat and is applied when the rendering is hard and dry.

The purpose of this coat is to bring the work to a true and even surface.

To accomplish this, plaster screeds are laid on the walls to serve as a guide, and along these a floating rule is traversed.

Screeds are usually laid near the ceiling or along the bottom edge of an intended cornice and at skirting level. Where door-frames and wood skirtings are to be fixed, wood grounds should be already in position so that the plasterer is able to work to these, for they will govern the thickness of the coatings. Vertical screeds are laid at internal and external angles. After the floating coat has been ruled fair, it is scoured over with a float, and when nearly hard it is scraped to form a roughened surface which will act as a key for the setting coat.

The third coat is termed a setting coat and is usually applied in one operation from floor to ceiling or cornice.

It should be well scoured with a hand float and trowelled over with a steel trowel, water being sprinkled on the surface as the work proceeds.

The setting coat should not exceed $\frac{1}{8}''$ in thickness.

When a rapid-setting rendering coat is desired, a mixture of 2 parts hydralime to 8 parts sand and 1 part Portland cement may be used.

Plaster cornices are usually formed to cover the angle between the wall and ceiling.

They may be run *in situ* or precast and fixed in position in lengths and mitre-jointed at angles and breaks. Plaster covings are often formed instead of cornices. They are built up in a manner similar to cornices, and when run *in situ* the angle between the wall and the ceiling is firred out with wood or metallic lathing.

Covings may be cast in fibrous plaster and erected in separate units.

External angles should be run with Keene's cement on a Portland cement backing.

Ceilings.—When plaster ceilings are to be formed under timber floor joists, the procedure should be lathing, pricking-up, rendering, floating and setting.

Wood laths are thin strips of wood which may be riven or sawn, the former being considered preferable to the latter.

They should be selected in lengths to suit the spaces between the joists and fixed end-butted and spaced about $\frac{3}{8}''$ apart, the material of the pricking-up coat being squeezed between the laths, thus securing a good hold for the finished ceiling.

Metallic Lathing

Expanded metal is used very extensively for lathing purposes, and particularly in the construction of suspended ceilings.

It is made from sheets of mild steel which are machine-cut

and drawn out, or expanded, thus forming a diamond-mesh appearance throughout the whole area of the sheet. In fixing, the metal is nailed to the underside of the floor joists and then pricked-up and covered with the rendering coat.

Plaster Sheets

Ceilings are sometimes formed by fixing fibrous or precast plaster slabs to the underside of the floor joists and then covering the sheets with a floating coat of gauged hair mortar and a thin setting coat of plaster or patent cement. The joints of the slab should be broken and preferably rebated and filled in with plaster or covered with wood battens.

When plaster slabs are to be covered with a floating and setting coats the surface of the slabs should be roughened to form a key for the finishing coats.

Partition Walls

The covering of partition walls should be carried out in a manner similar to brick walls and ceilings under wood-joisted floors.

Wood-stud partitions are first lathed with wood or metallic lathing and then pricked-up, rendered, floated and set.

Burnt-clay partition blocks are usually provided with dove-tailed grooves across the faces of the block, which form a key for the rendering coat.

Fibrous plaster slabs may be nailed to the framework of a wood-stud partition and then covered with a floating and setting coat as previously described.

CHAPTER XXII

MATERIALS

An outline of the Properties, Manufacture and Uses of the various Materials used throughout

Bricks

BRICKS may be classified by the materials used in their manufacture, method of moulding, burning, and the purpose for which they are made, viz. :

(1) Facing bricks.
(2) Engineering bricks.
(3) Common bricks.
(4) Special bricks.

Facing bricks comprise hand-made sand-faced reds, purples and greys and various machine-made bricks of suitable colours.

They should be made from malm or prepared marl in which the constituents are proportioned to give the best results. Multi-coloured facing bricks are used very considerably and are made in thicknesses varying from 1″ to 3″.

They are usually sand-faced, and moulded bricks can be obtained for arches, string courses, plinths, sills and coping.

Engineering bricks are a very heavy type of brick, smooth faced and well vitrified.

They are regular in size with sharp arrises and comprise Staffordshire, Southwater and Accrington types and are made for use where strength and damp-resistance are required.

Common Bricks.—This term refers to a large selection of machine-pressed wire-cut and hand-made bricks and includes Stocks, Flettons and local bricks of many varieties.

Common bricks may be clamp-burnt or kiln-burnt.

Stock brick is a term loosely applied to common bricks in general and in particular to London stocks, which are clamp-burnt and may be classified among the most durable bricks.

Fletton bricks are a common variety of pressed bricks which are made from shale in a semi-dry state, ground, screened and passed into a press, where they are subjected to a pressure of approximately 120 tons.

The shale contains almost sufficient fuel for the burning process, to which a small amount of coal is added. The bricks are burnt in continuous kilns and do not require to be previously dried.

Special Bricks

Fire-bricks are made from clays of a highly refractory nature ; they are capable of resisting high temperatures without fusion, and may be obtained in the form of tiles in sizes up to $18'' \times 12'' \times 2\frac{1}{2}''$ thick.

Glazed bricks are of two types:

    (1) Enamelled.

    (2) Salt glazed.

Enamelled bricks are obtainable in many colours. The enamelling is produced by partially burning the raw brick, then coating, by dipping its face in a vitreous slip made from ground flint and china clay with metallic oxides added.

The brick is then reburnt, this process being known as biscuiting.

The enamelling process may be commenced on the raw brick and the colour fixed in one burning, but large numbers are likely to be spoiled during burning.

Salt Glazed Bricks.—The glaze is obtained by throwing salt on the bricks while burning in the kiln.

The salt when volatilised by the heat penetrates into the pores of the exposed surfaces, thus covering them with a thin coating of glass.

Sand-lime bricks are made from chalk-lime mixed with clean sharp sand, the mixture being ground in mortar mills in a dry state.

Sufficient water is then added to produce cohesion, and the mixture is machine-pressed into bricks which are afterwards subjected to steam under pressure in a steel cylinder for about eight hours, which converts some of the sand with the lime into silicate of lime.

The bricks should be stacked for some months to harden before use.

Rubbers.—These bricks are made from finest malm, which contains a large quantity of sand.

They are lightly burnt and capable of being cut or evenly rubbed to shape. They are used chiefly for gauged brick-work in arches, etc., and for this reason they are usually supplied in larger sizes than ordinary bricks to allow for cutting and rubbing.

Purpose-made bricks are now made in many patterns for arches, plinths, string courses, squints, etc., and by their use much labour is saved and more accurate work is produced.

Fixing bricks are made from coke breeze or some synthetic materials which will allow of nails being driven into them for the fixing of door- and window-frames, skirtings and other joinery work.

Manufacture

Clamp-burnt Bricks.—The process of manufacture includes : clay-digging, washing and screening, the addition of chalk, sand and breeze as required, weathering, mixing and tempering in a pug mill.

The bricks are moulded, dried and burnt in clamps. They are usually unequal in quality, those on the outside of the clamp being underburnt, while those taken from the centre or near the firing eyes of the clamp are often overburnt and fused together forming ' burrs.'

Kiln-burnt Bricks.—These are more regular in quality than clamp-burnt bricks.

Many types of kilns are used in brick making, but the improved Hoffman kiln is the most successful type. These kilns ensure the production of a good-quality brick. The cycle of drying, burning and cooling, loading and unloading is practically continuous, and therefore economic in both fuel and time.

The process of manufacture through which the brick passes is as follows:

Clay-getting, washing, weathering, pugging, moulding, drying and burning in a kiln.

They are usually more regular in shape than a clamp-burnt brick, especially if they are machine moulded.

Wire-cut Bricks.—When the clay is obtained it is weathered and ground, pugged and pressed or squeezed through an orifice $4\frac{1}{2}'' \times 9''$ in section.

The strip of clay produced is cut into $3''$ blocks by means of wires arranged in a frame.

Wire-cut bricks are regular in form, and the wire marks are visible on both bed surfaces and frogs are omitted. These bricks are usually burnt in a kiln.

Sizes of Bricks

Although the face height of bricks may vary according to districts and architectural taste, the relation of length and breadth should be constant.

For the correct sizes of bricks reference should be made to the British Standard Specification for Dimension of Clay Facing and Backing Bricks, No. 657 (1936). This B.S.S. gives the following rule for the length and breadth of a brick:

Eight bricks, laid end to end, in contact, in a straight line:
  Maximum length $71''$
  Minimum ,, $69''$
Eight bricks laid side by side, in contact, in a straight line:
  Maximum length $34''$
  Minimum ,, $33''$
Eight bricks laid on edge, bedding surface to bedding surface, and back to back, in contact, in a straight line:
  Type 1: Maximum length $16\frac{1}{2}''$
       Minimum ,, $15\frac{1}{2}''$
  Type 2: Maximum ,, $21\frac{1}{2}''$
       Minimum ,, $20\frac{1}{2}''$
  Type 3: Maximum ,, $23\frac{1}{2}''$
       Minimum ,, $22\frac{1}{2}''$

Weight

Best pressed bricks and wire-cuts (with no frogs).—7 to 8 lb. each.

Common stocks.—6 to 7 lb. each.

Flettons.—5 to 6 lb. each.

Engineering bricks.—9 lb. each.

Mortar

Mortar is the material used in bedding and jointing bricks in forming brickwork, and its purpose is to increase the strength of the work by adhesion, and to provide a cushion or bed between the units comprising the wall.

It may be an admixture of sand and lime, sand and Portland cement, sand, lime and cement, or ground clinker and cement.

Lime mortar is made from Grey stone lime or hydrated lime in the proportion of 3 parts coarse sharp sand to 1 part lime, the sand being angular in grain and free from clay or dirt.

Lime mortars may be mixed by hand, but mill-mixed mortar is preferable, because the danger of refractory lumps being left in the mortar is eliminated.

The milling process may reduce the ultimate strength of the mortar slightly, but this is more than balanced by being thoroughly mixed.

Portland cement mortar known as " Compo " should be mixed as required and consists of 1 part Portland cement to 4 or 5 parts clean sand.

Portland Cement

Portland cement is an artificial cement produced by the mixing and calcination of certain materials which will yield silicates and aluminates of lime, and is obtained from the natural or mechanical combination of lime with silica and alumina in the form of shale.

Limestone and shale, when obtained in rock form, are first ground and then mixed in grinding mills with a correct proportion of clay which has been made into a slurry in a wash mill.

When this mixture leaves the mill, it is ground to a very

fine slurry, then elevated to storage tanks and conveyed to the feeding end of the kiln and delivered into the kiln in exactly the correct quantity. The slurry passes down through the rotary kilns, which are steel cylinders about 300′ long and 8′ to 10′ in diameter, lined with firebricks and slightly inclined to the horizontal.

At the lower end coal-dust is blown into the kiln where it is ignited and creates a fierce heat of about 1,700° C.

As the kilns rotate, the slurry is first dried and ultimately fused into the form of a clinker which is conveyed through a series of coolers to a storage plant.

Fusion takes place at a temperature of about 1,500° C. To the clinker is now added a small quantity of gypsum (from 1½ to 2½%), the addition of which controls the setting time of the cement.

The materials are then conveyed to grinding mills, where they are ground to a very fine powder and which is the final process of manufacture.

Provided that the materials are suitably selected and the various stages of manufacture properly carried out, the test of the quality of the cement is in its fineness.

For particulars regarding tests for fineness and setting time reference should be made to the B.S.S. for Portland cement No. 12 (1931).

Limes

The term lime is applied to several materials all of which are produced by calcining or burning some form of lime-stones, the product being named according to the composition of the limestones burned.

Quicklime is a term applied to lime which slakes readily and which is in the state in which it comes from the kiln.

Fat lime is a term applied to a pure lime which forms a plastic paste or putty when slaked by the addition of a suitable proportion of water.

It is made by burning limestone or chalk containing at least 96% of calcium carbonate.

Lean lime is the term applied to any lime which slakes on the addition of a suitable proportion of water but does not form a highly plastic putty.

Such limes are formed when any limestone containing more than 5% of silica is overburnt.

It is almost impossible to overburn a pure limestone or one that is free from silica.

Hydraulic lime is the term applied to any impure lime which possesses the property of setting, or forming a hard rock-like mass when mixed with a suitable proportion of water.

The most powerfully hydraulic limes contain approximately 65% lime, 10–13% alumina and 20–23% silica. According to their foreign content they may range from feebly to eminently hydraulic in properties.

They are made chiefly from a natural mixture of limestones, sand and clay, such as that constituting the greater part of the lias formation. For this reason they are often called ' lias limes.'

When an artificial mixture of limestone with a suitable clay is burnt the product is known as Portland cement.

CONCRETE

is the term applied to an aggregation of hard, coarse and solid substances which are bound together by a cement.

The former constituents are known as aggregates. The choice of aggregates is usually governed by cost, conditions and the available local materials, but hard broken stone, well-burnt bricks, gravel, ballast, furnace clinker and sand can be used, the latter being referred to as fine aggregate.

Concrete intended for use in positions where compressive stresses are likely to occur, as in foundation work, should comprise ballast, broken brick or stone aggregates, but when it is likely to be placed in positions where it is liable to be subjected to heat during an outbreak of fire, broken brick or furnace clinker aggregates are most suitable, because they will not change in structure. Ballast and broken stone aggregates are liable to fly when cold water is applied during a conflagration. Sand plays an important part in the ultimate success of concrete, as the small particles assist in filling the voids between the large aggregates and reduces the quantity of cement required for this purpose.

The sand should be clean and free from clay or organic matter.

The water used for mixing concrete should be fresh, clean, and free from organic or mineral impurities. The strength and other physical properties of dense concrete depend upon the ratio of water to cement.

Proportioning and Mixing

The proportions should be specified in terms of weight of cement to volumes of aggregate, because it is customary for cement to be delivered in bags or sacks of a specified weight.

A 112-lb. bag is roughly equal to $1\frac{1}{4}$ to $1\frac{1}{2}$ cubic ft., or 1 cubic ft. may be assumed to weigh 90 lb.

The correct proportioning of concrete will depend upon the stresses to which the concrete is likely to be subjected. For ordinary foundation work an admixture of 6–2–1, that is, 6 parts large aggregate, 2 parts sand or fine aggregates and 1 part Portland cement.

The aggregates should be screened between the limits of 2″ and $\frac{3}{8}$″ and for the finer aggregates $\frac{3}{8}$″ downwards. The above-mentioned proportion will produce good concrete, but the proportion can be altered to suit any particular but not inferior to 1 cwt. Portland cement to 10 cubit ft. of coarse and fine aggregate.

Concrete mixing is best carried out in mixing machines if large quantities are required.

These machines are of a rotary type, and they ensure an accurate proportioning and thorough hydration of the whole of the mix.

The exact amount of water relative to the cement is very difficult to ascertain, but it will be found in practice that the ideal quantity is such that will produce a very stiff workable concrete.

Water content of concrete can be compared and controlled by making slump tests.

For details of these tests, reference should be made to Building Science Books.

Roofing Slates

Slates are essentially metamorphosed rocks of sedimentary origin.

An essential characteristic of a slate is the existence of planes of cleavage, caused by intense lateral pressure, and which will permit the rock to be split into thin slabs.

A good slate should be hard and tough and give a sharp metallic ring when struck and not absorb water to any appreciable extent.

Colour is due to the mineral content and cannot be considered as a definite index to quality.

The textures of slates may be coarse or fine but rough-surfaced slates will usually weather better than smooth ones. Slate deposits are to be found in North Wales, South Wales, Cornwall, Westmorland and in some parts of Scotland. Westmorland slates vary considerably in size and require to be sorted to suit the type of slating required. They are coarse in texture, light green in colour and are usually arranged with graduated margins, which decrease in length from the eaves to the ridge.

Welsh slates are usually supplied in regular sizes, and in four grades in each colour, viz., best, medium, seconds and thirds.

The ' bests ' are usually thinner than the seconds and so on, therefore by using ' best ' slates the roof covering is lighter and may tend to economy in the size of the structural members of the roof.

These slates may be obtained in random sizes and laid on a roof in diminishing margins.

Slates are sold by count, viz., 1,200 per 1,000.

Roofing tiles are made from special brick clays and manufactured in a manner similar to kiln-burnt bricks and are subject to the same defects as terra-cotta during burning processes.

If they are over-burnt they will twist and warp, whereas under-burnt tiles will soon show signs of decay.

A good tile should be free from hair cracks, and ring distinctly when struck.

Tiles may be hand-made or machine-made, the former method producing tiles of the best appearance and weathering qualities.

The characteristics of a good roofing tile are density, toughness and incipient vitrification. They should be straight in their width but curved in their length, so that the tail of the tile will lie close on to the surface of the under tiles. Special tiles are made for ridges, hips, valleys, etc., and for use at open valleys, verges, etc.

Special tiles are also made for the double course at an eaves.

Plain tiles are sold by the net thousand, and they weigh about $2\frac{1}{4}$ lb. each, their size being $10\frac{1}{2}'' \times 6\frac{1}{2}'' \times \frac{1}{2}''$. 1,000 machine-made plain tiles will weigh 1 ton.

Pan-tiles may be either non-interlocking or interlocking in form, the former being hand-made and the latter machine-made.

The non-interlocking tile is first moulded flat and afterwards bent in the form of an S.

This type of tile has been used very largely for covering the roofs of sheds, etc. They are laid or bedded on cement mortar direct on the battens with a single head lap of $3''$ to $4''$ and a side lap of $2''$. A double course at an eaves is not necessary.

The interlocking form of pan-tile is now used very extensively for domestic buildings, and they are made in great variety of forms.

They are formed to interlock with the neighbouring tiles on all the four sides, and laid on a roof which has been close boarded and battened.

Building Stones

Building stones in general use may be classified as Granites, Sandstones, Limestones, Marbles and Slates, although they are classified geologically as :

    (1) Igneous Rocks.
    (2) Aqueous Rocks.
    (3) Metamorphic Rocks.

Granite is an igneous rock and is made up of granular crystalline particles which have been united into a compact mass by crystallisation from a fluid under extreme pressure, below the earth's surface.

The essential mineral constituents of granite are quartz, felspar and mica.

Quartz is the chief mineral constituent of granite, and may be regarded as chemically unalterable by atmospheric influence, but extreme changes in temperature may cause disruption of the surface of the rock.

Felspar occupies about one-half of the bulk of the rock and may contain potash, alumina, and silica, or soda and lime. The composition of the felspar is an important factor in the determination of the durability of a granite.

Mica is a hydrated silicate of aluminum and potassium, sodium and lithium.

It may be of the white variety known as ' muscovite ' or the dark variety known as ' biotite ' ; the latter is a source of weakness in a granite as it tends to decompose after exposure.

The hardness and crystalline texture of granites enables them to be polished, therefore they are suitable for all positions where hard wear is expected, e.g., for plinths, piers, columns and door jambs.

Granite is quarried in Devonshire, Cornwall and Scotland.

Among the best-known granites may be mentioned :

De Lank, Cornwall.	Peterhead, Scotland.
Penryn, Cornwall.	Rubislaw, Scotland.
Creetown, Scotland.	Sclattie, Scotland.
Kemnay, Scotland.	

Sandstones and Limestones come under the heading of aqueous rocks. They are sedimentary rocks, which have been formed in deposits by the agency of water or winds.

The durability of these stones depends upon the kind of cementing material by which the grains are held together.

Sandstones consist chiefly of round or angular grains of quartz, with occasionally other minerals. The grains of quartz may be cemented into a solid mass by silica, carbonate of lime, oxide of iron and alumina.

The quality of a sandstone depends upon (1) the nature of the grains ; (2) the quality of the cementing material. The size of the grains determines the texture of the stone, and this may vary from a fine-grained compact stone to a coarse grit stone.

The cementing material is the chief factor in determining the durability and hardness of sandstone.

Siliceous cements produce the most durable sandstone.

Calcareous cements will produce an easily worked stone, but it will be inferior from a weather-resisting point of view.

Sandstones may be used for general stone facings, sills, thresholds, copings, piers, etc., and they are quarried in Gloucestershire, Yorkshire, Derbyshire, Cheshire, Lancashire and Scotland.

The following list includes a few of the best-known sandstones :

Bramley Fall, quarried in Yorkshire.

Darley Dale, quarried in Derbyshire.

Forest of Dean, quarried in Gloucestershire.

Hailes, quarried near Edinburgh.

Hollington, quarried in Staffordshire.

Howley Park, quarried in Yorkshire.

Limestones

The general characteristic of limestones is the presence of a large proportion of carbonate of lime, formed chiefly by the accumulation of shells or calcareous skeletons of marine or fresh-water organism which were deposited as sediment in the waters of seas or lakes. The character of a limestone depends upon :

(1) The nature of the original grains, whether organic remains or oolitic aggregations.

(2) The extent of the recrystallisation of the matrix.

Oolitic limestones are of marine origin, the oolites resembling the roe of a fish and are the result of an accumulation of carbonate of lime round a small nucleus of fragmentary shells or grains of mud and sand.

The grains are oval in shape and may be seen with the naked eye.

The cementing material which holds the oolitic grains

together may be calcareous, siliceous or argillaceous, but calcareous cement should predominate.

The hardness of limestones differs with the character of the cementing material.

Oolitic limestones are the most serviceable and durable for general building purposes.

The suitability of limestones for various architectural uses depends upon their structure and colour.

They are quarried in Dorset, Somerset, Bath district, Lincolnshire, Rutlandshire, Gloucestershire. Among the best-known limestones which are suitable for general building purposes may be mentioned :

Ancaster, quarried in Lincolnshire.

Bath Stones, quarried near Bath.

Clipsham, quarried in Rutlandshire.

Ham Hill, quarried in Somerset.

Ketton, quarried in Lincolnshire.

Portland, quarried in Dorset.

Marbles and slates come under the heading of metamorphic rocks.

True marble is a limestone which has undergone recrystallisation accompanied by a complete alteration of the original texture as a result of the application of combined heat and pressure.

The beauty of polished marble depends upon the nature of the colouring matter and its disposition in streaks and veins throughout the rock.

The veins, markings and various colours are due to the inclusion of foreign substances, such as : carbonate of magnesium, clay, carbonaceous matter and metallic oxides.

Timber

The timber used for constructional and decorative work in building may be divided into two classes, viz.—(1) soft-wood, (2) hard-wood.

The term soft-wood includes firs, pines, larch, spruce and all cone-bearing trees.

In these timbers the annual rings are very distinct and the

pores are filled with resinous matter. The timbers of the softwood variety which come under the headings of Northern Pine and 'White Fir' are known as 'deal' or 'spruce.'

They are distinguished for their straightness in the fibre and for their excellent qualities for use in constructional work where they are likely to be subjected to tensional and transverse stresses. Under the heading of Northern Pine are included such timbers as Scotch Fir, Red Pine, Yellow Pine, Yellow Fir, Baltic Fir, and Baltic Pine.

They are grown in Norway, Sweden, Russia and Great Britain. These timbers are easily worked, and the knots, though prevalent, are usually sound and firm.

SPRUCE AND WHITE FIR.—This class of timber is inferior in quality to the group just mentioned, but the quality varies and in some instances the timber is quite suitable for certain types of constructional work such as formwork for concrete and temporary centering, etc.

It is very largely used for carpentry in work of a domestic character, but it should be properly selected and the loose knots and resin pockets avoided as far as possible.

Russian Deal may be considered among the best of the Northern Pine variety.

It is close grained and more free from sap and knots and can be used for internal and external joinery.

Douglas Fir or Oregon Pine from the west side of North America is reddish in colour, hard, strong and straight grained and very free from shakes, sap and large knots. This timber is often known as Columbian Pine.

Red Pine is used for internal joinery, panels, shelving, etc. It is grown in the northern parts of North America.

American Yellow or White Pine is white to pale yellow in colour and easily worked and is used for internal joinery.

Seasoning

All timber should be seasoned before being used in a building to eliminate as far as possible any liability of excessive shrinkage or swelling in the finished work. To season means to dry out the moisture contained in the green timber until the required moisture content is obtained. The process may be carried out by the following methods :

(1) **Natural Seasoning.**—The sawn timber is stacked in a well-ventilated position, but protected from the effects of sun and rain.

The disadvantage of this method is the time required for the process and its limitations.

(2) **Water Seasoning.**—Logs are placed in running water with the butt end facing upstream. While in this position the water passes through the pores of the wood and washes out the sap.

After a period of immersion the log is partially dried and converted into planks and sized timbers, and then subjected to natural seasoning as before described.

(3) **Heat Seasoning.**—Timber is stacked in a steam-heated chamber through which fresh warm air is circulated. The warm air carries off the requisite amount of moisture in a comparatively short time compared with natural seasoning, but unless the process is properly controlled this acceleration induces excessive shrinkage.

Growth.—Trees which produce timber are known as exogens or outward growers, the new wood being formed beneath the bark.

The section of a tree stem consists of :

(1) A central pith.

(2) Layers of wood fibre in the form of rings which are known as annual rings, each being considered to represent a year's growth, the heartwood being termed duramen and the sapwood alburnum.

(3) Transverse plates of cellular tissue known as medullary rays.

(4) The cambium layer is the sap-conveying and life-giving ring of fibre next to the bark.

(5) The bark or cortex is the protecting coat on the outside of the stem and covers the cambium layer. In the spring, moisture from the earth is absorbed by the roots and rises through the stem of the tree as sap, which feeds the leaf buds. These give off moisture and absorb carbon, which in turn

thickens the sap. In the autumn the sap returns to the roots and in the complete process adds a new layer of wood to the stem of the tree.

Decay

The main causes of decay in timber are :
(1) Exposure to alternate wet and dry conditions.
(2) Fungoid growth.

A correct choice of timber for use in positions where alternate wet and dry conditions prevail will assist in preventing decay.

Ventilation is essential if timber is to be preserved from the effects of dry rot because exposure to warm, damp, stagnant air will encourage and accelerate the fungoid growth, which causes the timber to decompose and crumble away.

Sheet Lead

Lead is a metal which is very malleable and soft and one which may be easily compressed and made to flow, thus lending itself to be readily worked, or bossed to various positions on a roof surface.

Malleability is the property of a metal, by virtue of which it may be rolled into sheets and beaten into various shapes without being torn or cracked.

Lead has very little elasticity and expands more readily than contracts.

Lead used for external plumbing may be milled or cast into sheets.

CAST SHEET LEAD is not used extensively at the present time because it is expensive and varies in thickness and is therefore more difficult to work.

It is made by pouring molten lead on to a prepared sand-bed casting frame, and the thickness of the sheet is obtained by striking off the superfluous metal before it has time to solidify.

MILLED SHEET LEAD is made by first casting a block of lead and when it has cooled sufficiently, it is passed backwards and forwards through a pair of steel rollers until it is reduced to a sheet about 1″ in thickness.

This sheet is then cut across in 6' lengths and rolled again between heated rollers until it is reduced to the thickness or weight required per square foot.

If the lead is pure and well milled it should be very soft and easy to work or ' boss ' up and of equal thickness throughout.

Milled Sheet Lead may be obtained in sheets 30' long × 7' wide, the thickness being regulated by the weight per square foot.

Sheet lead is used for the formation of gutters, flats, flashings, etc.

INDEX